Environmental Portraits

People Making a Difference for the Environment

by
Kim Sakamoto Steidl

illustrated by Lynn Hunt

Cover by Lynn Hunt

Copyright © 1993, Good Apple

ISBN No. 0-86653-745-7

Printing No. 98765432

Good Apple
1204 Buchanan St., Box 299
Carthage, IL 62321-0299

A Paramount Communications Company

Printed on recycled paper

Table of Contents

GA1460

Acknowledgements

Through this book, I've been fortunate to meet many wonderful people, full of interest, care, and hope for humanity and the future of our environment. This book would not have been possible without the contributions of:

UCSC Science Library
SouthWest Museum
Madelyn Pyeatt
David Nelson
Katje Cook
Walden Woods Project
Sheri Griffith
George Washington Carver Museum
Tuskegee Institute
Shirley Briggs and the Rachel Carson Council
TreePeople
Mark Wellman
Kevin Bell
Carl Anthony
Robin Cannon and Juanita Tate
Stephanie Yu
Jessica Heyn
Marianne Riedman
Naomi Rose
Sherrie Russell Meline
Larry Graff and the Banana Slug String Band
Larry Villella
Al Lewandowski
Dayton Hyde
Bill Tao

I would like to extend my thanks to Lynn Hunt, the very talented illustrator of this book. Lynn's sensitive artwork reflects a true understanding and appreciation of the beauty of nature.

Finally I would like to thank my husband Franz for his graphic design work and steadfast encouragement and my family for their loving support.

A Note for Teachers

From the Native Americans who first walked this land to modern day "eco-activists," there have always been people dedicated to protecting the earth and the life it sustains. People from many different backgrounds and viewpoints have worked to make our earth a healthier, safer and more beautiful place to live.

This book presents but a few of the people who have worked as individuals or in coalition with others to contribute a voice for environmental education and action in our country—people like Black Elk, Thoreau, Rachel Carson and Sam LaBudde. Each possesses a unique perspective but shares a common concern for nature and humanity. By helping children to understand the relationships between people and the environment at home, we can help lay the foundation for understanding the ecology of our global community.

The collection of profiles and projects in this book is intended to engage children and teachers in active experiences that stimulate creative thinking and invested discussion. Environmental issues are complex and need to be given plenty of time for dialogue and reflection. Use these supplemental materials to enrich your existing classroom curriculum, and tailor these activities to meet the needs and interests of your students.

GA1460

Suggestions for Using This Book

 Here are some tips on using this reproducible book with the environment in mind:
- Create only the number of copies of each profile or activity that you plan to use.
- Use recycled paper when possible.
- Allow children to work cooperatively in groups of two or three.

 Spark children's interest and curiosity about the environment by helping them to know who is working to make your community a healthy and safe place to live. Invite people who are actively addressing environmental problems in your area to come to your classroom and share their experiences.

 Find out more about the history of your community. Who were the people who first lived in the area? What plants and wildlife are indigenous to the area? What environmental changes have taken place in the last century?

 There are many different ways to use the materials in this book. Find what works best for your classroom. Some teachers may reproduce several different profiles and activities and allow the children to select the ones that interest them the most. Others may ask groups of children to work together on a single page. Still others may encourage children to come up with ideas of their own for related projects and activities. I've found that the most inventive and rewarding kinds of learning come from the children themselves.

 Inspire children to become active participants for maintaining and improving the environment in their own community. Have children brainstorm ideas for possible projects. Community service organizations and youth groups may be willing to sponsor or work with your class on the project.

 Children need to know that there is hope for improving the environmental problems in our world. Make time for children to discuss their concerns openly. News reports about holes in the ozone and massive oil spills may often bring about a sense of helplessness for both children and adults. Present children with the facts and explain what people are doing to address the problems. Let them know that people working together in a collective effort can make a difference in helping to make the world a healthy and safe place to live.

Environmental Decoding Key
(For Use with Word Decoding Activities)

Air

Biodiversity

Conservation

Deforestation

Earth

Food Chain

Garbage

Habitat

Incinerator

Jellyfish

Kelp

Land

Marine Life

Norwal

Ocean

People

Quicksand

Recycle

Solar

Trees

United States

Volcano

Water

Xeriscape

You

Zoology

GA1460

Environmental Time Line
Selected Events in American History to 1900

From ancient times to the present, traditional Native American nations have practiced living in harmony with nature.

1634   Plymouth Colony prohibits the setting of forest fires.

1681   William Penn, proprietor of Pennsylvania, declares that for every five acres of land cleared one acre must be left forested.

1739   Connecticut passes a law to create an annual closed season on deer hunting.

1804-06   Lewis and Clark venture out on their first American transcontinental exploration.

1831   Maria Martin, a painter, works with John James Audubon on the book *Birds of America*.

1832   George Catlin, a painter, proposes the idea of a national park.

1844   Graceanna Lewis anonymously publishes her book *Life in the Insect World*.

1845   Thoreau goes on retreat to Walden Pond.

1849   U.S. Department of the Interior is established.

1857   Frederick Law Olmsted develops New York's Central Park.

1864   Yosemite Valley in California is reserved as a state park.

1872   Yellowstone in Wyoming becomes the first national park.

1892   Sierra Club is founded by John Muir.

1892   Henry S. Salt publishes an early book on animal rights.

1898   Gifford Pinchot becomes the head of the Division of Forestry.

GA1460

Black Elk
Traditional Native
American Views and the Environment

Black Elk was an Oglala Sioux from the northern Great Plains. He was a medicine man who helped to care for his people. In 1931 he told his life story in the book *Black Elk Speaks.*

Black Elk was born in 1863. Very early in life, he was taught that the land he lived upon was sacred. The Sioux, like many other Native American nations, believed that people were a part of nature's life cycle. Black Elk knew that plants and animals and other living things should be respected. When a bison was killed, he watched as the hide was made into blankets, the meat was eaten or preserved, and every part of the animal was put to use.

As an adult, he watched as the last of the bison were slaughtered by hunters who were only interested in making money from the hides of the animals or simply killing for sport. Black Elk was deeply concerned. He saw what was happening as a sign of problems with nature. He saw the way nature's cycle was not being cared for. He described what he saw as a "breaking of the sacred hoop of life." He warned of the dangers of treating life with such little respect and understanding. Few at the time heeded his words, but today, as his predictions are coming true, his words are read with new interest.

Black Elk's people once lived at peace with the earth. They hunted, fished, trapped and gathered what they needed for food and shelter. At times they changed the environment with the use of controlled grassland and forest burning. Yet, the Sioux and other Native American nations seemed to have realized that people do have an impact on the environment. Without a doubt, Native Americans can be called the first American environmentalists.

John G. Neihardt. *Black Elk Speaks: Being the Life Story of a Holy Man of the Oglala Sioux* (Lincoln, NE: University of Nebraska Press, 1961)

Black Elk Activities

Black Elk was a member of the Oglala Sioux nation from the northern Great Plains. There are many different nations of Native American Indians in this country, each with its own distinct customs, language and location. Yet, the traditional cultures of all the nations practiced balancing the needs of humans and the resources of nature.

Is not the sky a father and the earth a mother, and are not all living things with feet or wings or roots their children?

Black Elk
from *Black Elk Speaks*, 1931

What do you think Black Elk was trying to explain in the quote above? How would you describe the relationship between the earth, sky and living things? Write your ideas down and share them with someone you know.

There are more than 500 different Native American Indian groups in the United States according to the *Encyclopedia of the American Indian* (1990). This number includes more than 197 different Alaskan Native Americans as well.

See if you can find twelve of the nations in the word search below.

```
A   Z   E   N   O   L   H   O   Z
O   L   I   J   A   K   I   U   C
G   E   E   K   O   R   E   H   C
A   I   O   U   X   R   U   T   E
P   T   N   U   T   M   N   I   H
A   P   O   U   A   I   N   R   O
P   I   B   S   I   U   A   V   P
S   E   H   I   Z   T   U   N   I
C   H   E   Y   E   N   N   E   M
E   N   O   H   S   O   H   S   A
```

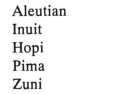

Aleutian	Cherokee	Chumash
Inuit	Ohlone	Sioux
Hopi	Cheyenne	Papago
Pima	Shoshone	Ute
Zuni	Crow	Apache

First Environmentalists
Making a Difference Today

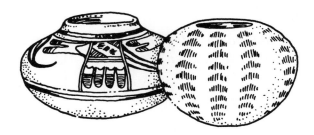

For many years Hopi burial sites have been invaded by "pot hunters." Pot hunters are people who dig up the burial sites in search of human remains and artifacts. In 1990 the Arizona legislature passed a law protecting Native American burial sites that **Vernon Masayesva**, chairman of the Hopi nation, drafted and helped promote to passage.

Winona La Duke, a Mohawk and president of the Indigenous Women's Network, is an activist for safe living conditions for Native American women. She has informed Native American communities in the Northeast about poisoned water supplies from local rivers and other toxic hazards. Thanks to Winona, many families are safe from drinking and using polluted water in their homes.

David Nelson is working to make sure that the Lakota children at the Cheyenne River Reservation have a clean and healthy environment to grow up in. He is planning to get more environmental education programs into the schools at Cheyenne River. David teaches his own children by example. When he goes out hunting or fishing, he picks up the trash that others have left behind.

Madelyn Pyeatt is proud of her Blackfoot heritage. She shares her heritage with high school students from Oakland, California. Many of those students are Native American as well. About twice a month, Madelyn loads up her truck with enough camping and rafting gear for a weekend. In the Sierra wilderness, she helps students learn to read maps, identify plants and wildlife, and act safely on the trail. She also gives lessons in history as she tells students about the native people who once lived in the area.

GA1460

Graceanna Lewis
Quaker Naturalist

Family and friends always encouraged young Graceanna Lewis to study the things she loved most. They knew very well that she was interested in learning about nature. She spent many hours investigating the plant and animal kingdom, but had no idea that someday she would become a leading American naturalist.

Graceanna Lewis was born on August 3, 1821, into a Quaker family from Chester County, Pennsylvania. Her father died when she was three years old, and her mother, Esther, taught Graceanna and her three sisters to be keen observers of the natural world. Together, they would keep records of the weather and the growth of plants on their farm. They also kept an astronomy diary that recorded comets, meteors, eclipses and other observations of the night sky.

When Graceanna went off to boarding school, she studied botany and astronomy. She knew so much about the subjects that she became a science teacher. In her letters home she would write about the discovery of new plants or constellations.

In 1847 Esther died. Graceanna missed her mother very much. She returned home to Chester County and took care of her sisters and helped to run the family farm. The Civil War was about to begin, and there was little time to spend on nature. Instead, Graceanna, like many other Quakers, became involved in the movement against slavery.

After the war, Graceanna found the time to study nature once again. Friends such as Marie Mitchell, a Quaker astronomer, and John Cassin, an ornithologist, helped by giving her books, microscopes and other scientific instruments. They encouraged her to make a living by studying and teaching about nature.

Taking her friends' advice, Graceanna started a full-time career as a naturalist. At first, she wasn't taken seriously as a scientist because most people believed that women should not take jobs outside of the home, and especially not in the field of science. Many times, she was overlooked for a job because she was a woman. Graceanna found herself actively working for the women's movement in the late 1800s, in addition to her writing and teaching.

Graceanna Lewis became known as a leading nineteenth-century American naturalist. She was raised to believe that each person has something important to contribute to the world. Her understanding of the natural world and the people in it proved that she was not only a woman of science, but also a woman of conscience.

GA1460

Graceanna Lewis Activities
The Natural Sciences

Graceanna Lewis was a Quaker. Quakers have a long history of practicing peaceful ways of resolving problems. They also believe that learning is a lifelong process from "cradle to grave." Both women and men are given a voice and encouraged to study and speak out.

How might being a Quaker during the nineteenth century have affected Graceanna Lewis and her life as a naturalist?

Think about and study what roles men and women usually had during the nineteenth century in our country. Are these roles different now? How are they the same or different?

Graceanna was interested in many kinds of natural science. See if you can guess each type of natural science from its definition.

The science that deals with the origin, history, behavior and physical characteristics of plants and animals

The study of plants, their life, structure, growth and classification

The science related to zoology that involves the study of insects

The branch of science dealing with finding out about oceans

The study of birds

The science of the stars that investigates such aspects as their motion, position in space, size and composition

* * * * * * * *

What is your favorite kind of science? If you like helping animals, veterinary science might be something you would be interested in. Computer science is another popular field these days. Try inventing one if you don't have a favorite yet. How about sportsfanology, which is the study of the way fans behave at sporting events? Define your science and describe what you enjoy about it.

Refer to the Decoding Key on page vi to help you solve the puzzle below.

___ ___ ___ ___   ___ ___ ___ ___ ___   ___ ___ ___ ___.

6

GA1460

Henry David Thoreau
The Nature of Words

In his book, *Walden*, Thoreau wrote that he went to live in the woods to try to learn about what was basic in life. He wanted to live away from what he saw as a world of people interested only in material things. He was fed up with the way people held attitudes of prejudice and acted for the sake of appearances. Thoreau's work gave people an understanding of how nature and human beings are a part of one another. He once said, "In wildness is the preservation of the world."

The work of Henry David Thoreau has inspired many naturalists and environmentalists, from John Muir to William O. Douglas. Today many people share the way that Thoreau looked at and understood nature, but during his time most people held different attitudes.

The year was 1845 when Henry David Thoreau decided he had chopped down all of the pines that he would need to frame his new cabin in Walden Woods near Concord, Massachusetts. This was the first house he had ever owned. It was 10 feet wide and 15 feet long. The cabin held the basics of a bed made of cane, a table, desk, three chairs, some cooking and eating utensils, and a lamp. His bathtub and refrigerator was Walden Pond.

Each day he walked about the woods identifying plants, wildlife and insects. He measured the banks of snow that built up in the winter and the depth of the pond with each passing season. He collected samples of moss, bark and beetles to examine in his cabin. He kept a journal and wrote down his thoughts and findings. Sometimes, he would take his rowboat and sit out in the moonlight, drift along and play his flute, or sit in the sun enjoying the smell of pine and sumac. He tried to use all of his senses to understand and experience nature.

In the nineteenth century, most people saw nature as a threat to people. Settlers who had to carve their homesteads into the wilderness and survive blizzards, droughts, floods, and fire, saw nature as something to be tamed. Henry was a gentleman used to a very comfortable life-style, and he had never experienced such hardship. Henry David Thoreau was a nature philosopher. His time at Walden Pond gave him time to think and write about the way that people looked at nature in the past. Many people who once thought of the wilderness as a place to fear began to see hope and beauty through the words of Henry David Thoreau.

GA1460

Henry David Thoreau Activities

Thoreau believed that people who lived in towns and cities needed to get to know nature in the wilderness. He thought that living in highly populated areas, people became more interested in buying and showing off material goods. Thoreau thought that the wilderness helped people understand what was really valuable in life. He saw Walden Woods as a place to inspire strength and creativity.

Make a list of five objects that you would like to own. Add the brand names and prices of the objects if you can. Write down why each of these items is important to you.

Make a list of five objects that you might need to survive in the wilderness for a month. Add the cost of each item if you can. Write down why each of these things would be important to you.

Compare the two lists of items that you have just made. What items are the same? What items are different? Discuss the choices you made in small groups of three or four.

The Walden Woods Project

The Walden Woods Project was founded in 1990. The purpose of the organization is to purchase and protect the area known as Walden Woods near Concord, Massachusetts. Each year, more than 500,000 people visit Walden Pond and Walden Woods. They come to see the cabin where Thoreau did much of his writing, walk in the woods and enjoy the natural beauty of the land.

One reason why the area has been protected is because of the support of celebrities, environmentalists and the general public. Ed Begley Jr., Lou Diamond Phillips and Whoopi Goldberg are just some of the people who have been involved with the Walden Woods Project.

Refer to the Decoding Key on page vi to help you solve the puzzle below.

8

John Muir and Gifford Pinchot
Respecting Each Other's Differences

John Muir

John Muir and Gifford Pinchot were two men who held very different ideas about the environment. John Muir believed that the wilderness should be *preserved*. Gifford Pinchot thought that the environment should be *conserved*. Both men were leaders in the environmental movement during the nineteenth century.

John Muir was a naturalist, explorer and writer who campaigned for the preservation of the American wilderness. He was born on April 28, 1838, in Dunbar, Scotland. At the age of eleven, his family moved to the United States. Living on a farm in Wisconsin, John learned about the beauty and usefulness of nature. As an adult, he founded the famous Sierra Club. His many books (like *The Mountains of California* and *Our National Parks*), articles and speeches helped to create many protected wilderness areas including Yosemite National Park. To John, the wilderness was a place to be respected and revered without the intrusion of humankind. He saw foresters and other conservationists as meddling intruders into nature's world.

Gifford Pinchot was the first American to take up the profession of forestry and the first head of the U.S. Forest Service. He was outspoken in his manner and known to appoint women and African Americans to office during a time when most governmental leaders did not. He was born in 1865 to a wealthy family from Pennsylvania. He was educated in the best schools and traveled to Europe where he learned about the concept of conservation in forestry. Gifford helped to popularize the idea of conservation in the United States. He believed that public wilderness areas could be used as a source of income for the country if the resources were handled wisely. As head of the Forest Service, he traveled all over the country educating people about the many uses of public lands, such as grazing, agriculture and lumbering.

Although John Muir and Gifford Pinchot had many disagreements about how public lands should be treated, they often found themselves working together on projects for the environment. Once they went on a government trip to the Grand Canyon. Several people interested in the future of the area attended the overnight expedition. As the two men walked together along a rocky canyon trail, they spotted a tarantula. Gifford raised his boot to step on the creature. John stopped Gifford by telling him that the tarantula had just as much right to be on the trail as they did. That evening, the two stayed up until midnight telling each other stories about their adventures in the wilderness.

Gifford Pinchot

John Muir and Gifford Pinchot Activities

Preservation and Conservation

Think about the two views of preservation and conservation held by John Muir and Gifford Pinchot. What do these two views have in common? What makes these two views different?

Draw an imaginary wilderness area. Use your creativity to design mountains, plateaus, canyons, rivers, lakes, oceans and streams. Include the plant and animal life common in the area. You decide if it will be a desert, rain forest, ocean, mountain or glacial region, or a combination of these areas.

Write a statement about how people may use this area. Will the area be completely protected from people or will you allow some development and use of natural resources? Think about uses for recreation (what kinds will be allowed), development (buildings, homes and businesses) and profits from natural resources (mining, timber, oil drilling). Write your statement as clearly as possible, covering the different kinds of uses allowed on your area.

Take all of the different wilderness areas that your class has drawn and connect them together. You now have an imaginary country waiting to be occupied by people from other areas.

Create a class policy on a way to make room for the new people while protecting the natural resources of your country. Make sure that every person in your class has a voice in creating the policy.

What is the fairest way to make these kinds of decisions?

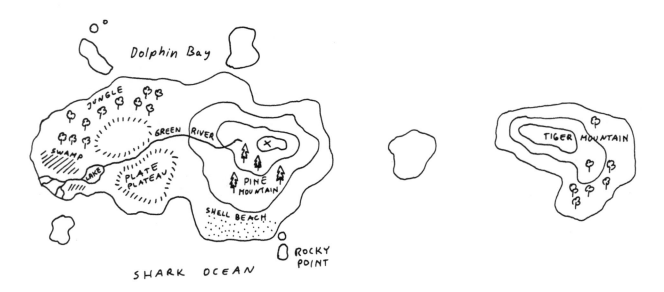

GA1460

Mary Hunter Austin
A Little Different Than Most

Mary Hunter Austin was born in 1868 in Carlinville, Illinois. As a child, family and friends talked about her as being "different." Mary was different from most nineteenth century young girls. When she felt that something was not fair, Mary spoke out about it. She had a creative mind and shared her ideas with others. It wasn't easy for Mary to grow up during a time when most children were expected to be seen and not heard.

The Land of Little Rain was the first of Mary's books. The book was a collection of stories that told about people and the earth. In one story, she wrote about a man who wandered through the desert and mountains when a terrible blizzard hit. The man lost his way and searched for shelter. When darkness fell, he saved himself by lying down next to what he thought was a flock of ranch sheep. When the man awoke, he discovered himself surrounded by wild bighorn sheep, one of the shyest of all animals. Mary believed that by writing books like *The Land of Little Rain* she could help people understand the wonder and wisdom of living with nature.

In the early 1900s, Mary moved to the Owens Valley, an area that lies just east of the Sierra Nevada Mountains. The government Bureau of Reclamation and the city of Los Angeles had made a plan to bring water from the Owens Valley to Los Angeles. Mary knew that the way of life for many of the sheepherders, farmers and prospectors who lived in the Owens Valley would come to an end. She felt that changing the water route for the sake of creating a big city was not respectful to nature and could lead to many problems in the environment. Mary found that there were few who believed as she did. Even Gifford Pinchot, a fellow conservationist, supported the idea of diverting the water. The plan to route the water to Los Angeles was passed.

Mary warned of the dangers that might come by upsetting the balance of nature: pollution, overpopulation and destruction of natural resources. At that time some laughed at her, but sadly many of her predictions have come true.

Mary Hunter Austin Activities
Women and Nature

Women have always been a part of the search for understanding and caring for the environment. In the nineteenth and early twentieth centuries, American women were rarely recognized for their knowledge of natural history. Some learned about it from firsthand experience, such as Native American women, early pioneer women and women who worked the gold rush. Others chose to express their understanding through writing, drawing, painting and other forms of art.

Sacajawea was a sixteen-year-old Shoshoni woman. She acted as an interpreter and peacemaker to the explorers Lewis and Clark in the early 1800s. Her understanding of the people and the land allowed for the safe passage of the Lewis and Clark party. She died of a fever along the Upper Missouri River a few years later.

Susan Fenimore Cooper was a talented nineteenth century writer. Her book, *Rural Hours*, was one of the first nature books written in North America. Based on her own daily nature journal, the book was a great success. Susan, the eldest of James Fenimore Cooper's children, was recognized as an author in her own right.

Ines Mexia was a Mexican American botanist who started her work at the age of fifty-five. Living at the turn of the twentieth century, Inez was known as one of the most prolific collectors of her time. On one trip, she brought back more than thirteen thousand botanical specimens from Mexico.

Calamity Jane has been described as a "free spirit" of the West. Born Martha Jane Cannary in 1852, she held many jobs such as a scout, cowgirl, sharpshooter, stage driver and stuntwoman. She was also a caring wife to Wild Bill Hickok and a mother. She loved the wilderness and felt comfortable being a part of it.

Find out more about these and other women who lived during the nineteenth and early twentieth centuries.

Find out more about women today who are active in the environmental movement. Here are some names to get you started:

Winona LaDuke	activist for Native American women's rights
Lois Marie Gibbs	founder of Citizens Clearinghouse for Hazardous Waste
Rebecca Flores	activist against use of toxic pesticides in agriculture
Anne La Bastille	writer and woodswoman
Sheri Griffith	river outfitter and conservationist
Jane Goodall	scientist who studies chimpanzees in the wild

GA1460

Mary Hunter Austin Activities
Pinecone Puzzle

Use only the letters you find in the pinecone and see how many nature words you can come up with. Here are a few examples to get you started:

e __ __ __ __ gy   w __ __ __ d   e __ __ th   __ __ __ ure

t __ __ __ s   __ __ __ ects   w __ __ er   s __ __ ar

__ __ il   c __ __ __ ost   __ __ __ ds   w __ __ d

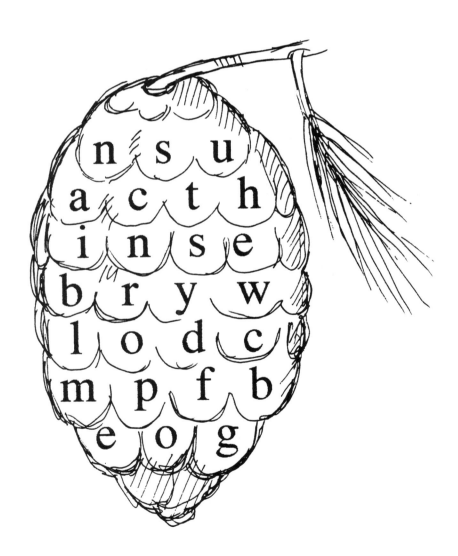

George Washington Carver
A Resourceful Inventor

Most people remember George Washington Carver as the famous African American botanist. He was known for inventing and popularizing uses for the peanut and sweet potato plant. Many say that it was his resourcefulness that helped him to become such a creative inventor.

George Washington Carver was born into slavery on a farm in Missouri in the late 1800s. Orphaned when he was just a baby, he was raised by Susan and Moses Carver, the owners of the farm. Growing up, George always felt that he had a way with plants. Many hours of his childhood were spent in the woods collecting samples of flowers to be transplanted in his garden. He soon became known as the "plant doctor."

After emancipation, George tried his hand at homesteading in Kansas. From there, he attended college and earned his bachelor of science degree in 1894. In his early thirties (the exact date of his birth is unknown), he took a job as an assistant botanist at Ames Experiment Station in Iowa. A few years later, Booker T. Washington asked George to head a new agricultural experiment station at Tuskegee Institute in Alabama. George agreed by saying, "Of course it has always been the one great ideal of my life to be of the greatest good to the greatest number of 'my people' possible." He felt that education was the answer for true freedom for the African American people.

At the turn of the century when George began his work at Tuskegee College, he was given a small space at the college's Experiment Station. There was little money to fund the laboratory so George had to rely on his own resources and inventiveness to find the necessary equipment to conduct his experiments. Glass food jars became laboratory beakers, bits of old rope held plants and stakes together,

and crates were turned into furniture. He soon gained a reputation at the college of collecting things that others threw away.

In 1903, George began raising a few Spanish peanut plants at the Experiment Station. He was eventually credited with helping to develop more than 200 peanut products. He used everything from the shells, the oil and the peanut itself. In addition to the peanut, he also invented many uses for the sweet potato. George Washington Carver practiced recycling and reusing in his experiments and his daily life.

GA1460

George Washington Carver Activities
Recycling and Reusing

George Washington Carver was especially resourceful when it came to recycling and reusing items that others did not find useful anymore. Describe some things that you have created new uses for in the past. Making a quilt, using an old broomstick handle to play stickball and turning yesterday's leftovers into a deliciously different meal are just a few examples of reusing and recycling right in your own home.

George Washington Carver created and made note of more than a hundred products created from peanuts. Set a time limit for yourself and make a list of as many different products using peanuts as you can imagine. Compare your answers with your friends'.

Get some peanuts and sweet potatoes and make some of your own products. Some suggestions might be a peanut butter shake, sweet potato stamps using food coloring as ink, sweet potato pie made from the sweet potato stamps, or honey roasted peanuts.

Environmental Time Line
Early Twentieth Century

1905   The National Audubon Society is founded.

1907   Gifford Pinchot becomes the head of the new U.S. Forest Service.

1908   The Grand Canyon becomes an official national monument.

1916   The National Parks Service is established.

1924   Aldo Leopold has Gila National Forest in New Mexico designated as the nation's first major wilderness area.

1924   Mardy and Olaus Murie begin a lifelong partnership studying the wilderness.

1933   Civilian Conservation Corps is formed to provide jobs and maintain public lands during the Great Depression.

1934   Roger Tory Peterson's *A Field Guide to the Birds* is published.

1939   William O. Douglas is appointed to the Supreme Court. He speaks out for conservation and the belief that natural objects have legal rights.

1940   U.S. Bureau of Land Management is established. The government agency was created to take care of public lands.

1942   Jacques-Yves Cousteau and Emile Gagnan invent the automatic regulator, or Aqualung™. Scuba diving equipment is based on the technology of the automatic regulator.

1949   *A Sand County Almanac* by Aldo Leopold is published. The book is a collection of essays that talk about ecology and a new way of thinking about the land.

1950s   Barry Commoner is one of the first scientists to warn against the atmospheric testing of nuclear weapons.

1962   Rachel Carson alerts the world to the dangers of abusing chemical pesticides in her book *Silent Spring*.

1964   The National Wilderness Preservation System is established by the Wilderness Act.

1966   The Endangered Species Act allows for federal involvement to protect habitats and identify rare species. The 1973 Endangered Species Act allows for added protection of plants and wildlife.

1969   Friends of the Earth is founded by David R. Brower.

1969   Greenpeace is organized.

GA1460

Mardy and Olaus Murie
A Life in the Wilderness

Mardy closed the cabin door behind her. She could see her breath as she stepped out into the cool Alaskan air. The dogs were harnessed and ready to go. Neighbors came out of their cabins to say good-bye. Mardy joined her husband, Olaus, next to the dogsled. Olaus gave the command and soon the newlyweds were off, gliding over the ice toward the Koyukuk River. This 1924 trip would mark the beginning of a lifelong partnership studying the wilderness for Mardy and Olaus Murie.

In the valley below, Mardy saw the Koyukuk River winding its way through groves of cottonwoods. Two weeks of traveling in the Alaskan wilderness were left. Their goal was the far off snow-covered Endicott Mountains. The sled jostled and bucked as it went over stumps and hollows in the trail. At times, the sled would tip over with Mardy flying into the snow. The couple traveled about nineteen miles each day. At night the couple camped next to the river. While Olaus gathered spruce boughs to make a mat for their sleeping bags, Mardy cooked up dinners of rabbit, fried potatoes and beans.

When they reached the Endicott Mountains, Mardy and Olaus set up the ten-foot-square tent that would become their winter home.

Olaus was a wildlife biologist. His job during this trip was to study caribou. The Muries followed the habits of the caribou and recorded their findings. For many months they collected caribou specimens, recorded their winter habits, and observed their migration patterns. For Mardy and Olaus, the wilderness was never a lonely place. They were comforted by the echo of tree branches falling, the smell of food cooking on the camp stove, the stars shining through the spruce trees at night, and most of all, each other.

The trip to the Endicott Mountains would be the first of many expeditions for the Muries. They traveled, often with their children, into the Arctic and the Wyoming wilderness with only the basics for living. The data that they collected became the basis for their conservation work. They wrote articles and books, gave speeches and testified in hearings to protect the wilderness. The Muries helped to make sure that places like the Arctic National Wildlife Range and the North Cascades National Park were established. In 1963, Olaus Murie died. Mardy felt alone without her trail mate and husband, but continued on with the conservation work they had started so many years ago near the Koyukuk River.

17

GA1460

Mardy and Olaus Murie Activities
Science of Teamwork

Mardy and Olaus Murie were a great team as they lived and worked in the wilderness. Mardy would work at the base camp while Olaus went on field assignments to collect specimens or observe the behavior of animals. Together, they set up their tent and chopped wood for fuel. Their survival depended on solid teamwork.

🌲 Think about a time when you were a part of a group that worked well together. It might be a time when you and a friend built a clubhouse, or your family made a meal together.

🌲 🌲 Describe what happened. How did you share your responsibilities? Did one person come up with all of the ideas, or did all the members contribute suggestions? How did you feel after you were finished?

🌲 🌲🌲 Describe a time when you found it really difficult to work with others. What happened? What seemed to go wrong? What might you do differently next time?

Here are some sample specimen descriptions. See if you can tell what animal each belongs to.

1. A thin barbed quill about five inches in length. Dark brown in color.

2. A tuft of black and white striped fur. It has a strong offensive odor.

3. A clump of mouse fur and bones that were once ingested.

4. A small branch from a pine tree with a hard brown seed pod attached.

5. A set of horns spanning four feet across. There are six sharp points on each side.

6. A clump of tiny orange eggs less than one centimeter in diameter. They were found in the river.

GA1460

Aldo Leopold
Learning from Mistakes

Aldo Leopold was born in 1887 to a German American family who loved the great outdoors. Aldo's grandfather was a naturalist and taught him about the many different kinds of birds that migrated over their home in Burlington, Iowa. His father taught him about the responsibility of hunting for recreation, and his mother helped him understand the beauty of nature. Much of his youth was spent exploring and hunting in the woods and marshes along the Mississippi River.

At sixteen, Aldo went on to study the science of forestry at Yale University. After he graduated, he took a job with the Forest Service in the New Mexico and Arizona territories. He enjoyed speaking with local hunters, ranchers and foresters about creating game refuges. He believed that sport hunters should take part in protecting the wilderness where they hunted.

Many events helped to shape Aldo's attitude about humans and their relationship with nature. Early in his career, Aldo worked to form a policy that allowed the killing of wolves and mountain lions in the Southwest. He felt that by killing these natural predators, the number of deer would increase for sport hunting. He even went hunting and killed wolves himself.

Many years later, he heard reports that the deer population in the Southwest had grown out of hand. The large number of deer had damaged vegetation and the animals were threatened with starvation. The Forest Service ordered a road cut through the protected Gila wilderness and hunters were allowed in to reduce the deer population. Aldo deeply regretted his decision to eliminate the wolves and mountain lions.

He spent the rest of his life with a changed attitude about the role of people and nature. He felt that his early efforts at conservation did not work because he had an attitude that people could do anything they wanted with the land. After changing his attitude, Aldo believed that the soil, water, plants and animals (including people) of the land were all connected. He saw that all the elements represented important links in a chain that kept the earth a healthy place to live. If one link was weakened, then the strength of the whole chain would be threatened.

Aldo Leopold was a conservationist who believed that people could learn from their mistakes. His ideas about conservation helped Americans understand that the wilderness is a very precious and necessary resource.

GA1460

Aldo Leopold
The Gray Wolf

A story written by the late Chief Dan George tells of a Native American grandfather who took his grandson into the forest to learn how to call wolves. The grandfather sang the ancient words and the young boy listened closely. They waited for the wolves, but none came. The grandfather repeated the ceremony once again. Still, no wolves came to them. The grandfather wondered why, and then realized that there were no more wolves.

The gray wolf, also known as the timber wolf, once roamed freely throughout many parts of the country. Shy of humans, the wolves did not stand a chance against bounty hunters, farmers and ranchers who saw them as a threat to livestock and deer. Shotguns, traps and strychnine were used to reduce their population by staggering numbers. Montana alone recorded 80,000 wolves killed between 1884 and 1918. It was not until 1973 that the gray wolf, close to extinction, was placed on the endangered species list. As a result, their numbers are slowly rising in Alaska, Idaho, Michigan, Minnesota, Montana, Washington and Wisconsin.

In many cultures, the wolf has been a symbol of fear. From English fairy tales to legends of the old west, the wolf was stereotyped as evil and frightening. People believed that wolves had special powers, and even today people have been known to hunt them unlawfully.

There are several groups in the country that work to inform the public about wolves. In Wisconsin, the Timber Wolf Alliance is a group that helps kids and adults get the real facts about wolves. This organization lets people know that wolves play an important part in maintaining the balance of nature. They help to keep in check populations of deer, bison and other animals that wolves feed upon. They do not kill for the sake of killing itself, but only for food. In the past, they have sometimes killed unguarded livestock but have rarely been a threat to humans.

The Timber Wolf Alliance has even helped to inspire kids to take action. A few years ago, some fifty students at Mead Elementary School in Wisconsin Rapids, Wisconsin, sold audio tapes and videotapes to support the organization. The kids also got together and sent out more than 300 questionnaires to find out what people thought about the idea of wolves being introduced into the Wisconsin wilderness. Then they wrote down their findings in letters to the state lawmakers. With kids like these on their side, the future looks hopeful for the gray wolf.

Aldo Leopold Activities
Wolf Mythology and the Gray Wolf

Get together in small groups and come up with a list of stories, myths or legends that involve wolves. Talk about where these ideas might have come from.

Choose one story idea to act out in your class. Write out scripts as a writing project or work by improvisation.

Next, write down some true facts about wolves.

Present your story to the class and then ask some members of the class to give one or two true facts of their own about wolves.

True or False

1. Wolves are often shy of humans.	true	false
2. Wolves have been known to attack livestock.	true	false
3. Wild wolves can be trained as reliable pets.	true	false
4. Every species that was in Yellowstone is still there except for the wolf.	true	false
5. The wolf is an endangered species.	true	false

Thinking About the Issues

Renee Askins, founder of The Wolf Fund, is working to bring the wolves back to Yellowstone. She believes that they have a right to be in the wilderness areas of the park and will help to provide a balance to the ecosystem by keeping deer and antelope herds in check. She says the wolf has been stereotyped by hundreds of years of bad press. She thinks of the wolf as a symbol of the West.

Pete Story, a rancher near Yellowstone, believes that the wolf is a vicious killer. He says that once the wolves get used to Yellowstone, they'll lose their fear of humans.

Those are just two opinions. What do you think? Write down your ideas and hold small group dialogues on the topic. Have students represent many different sides of the issue. Use resources from your school library, and think about the issues before your dialogue.

Roger Tory Peterson: Making Connections
Ornithologist and Artist

Roger Tory Peterson was born in Jamestown, New York, in 1900. When he was in the seventh grade, he joined his school's Junior Audubon Club. Each child was given a paper with an outline of a bird. The children were supposed to color the birds with crayons. Mrs. Hornbeck, Roger's teacher and the club leader, decided that coloring in the outline of a bird was not the way to learn how to draw birds.

One day, Mrs. Hornbeck brought in a collection of bird paintings by the artist and naturalist Louis Agassiz Fuertes. The paintings showed birds of many different kinds in full color. They seemed so real and full of life. Roger had never seen anything like them before. Mrs. Hornbeck passed out a painting and a box of watercolors to each child. Roger got to paint a picture of a blue jay. That was Roger Tory Peterson's first bird painting. To this day, the blue jay is still his favorite bird. By the age of seventeen, Roger had become so skilled at painting birds that a bird club in New York City exhibited one of his paintings. For three weeks, he had worked on a painting of a kingbird, making sure that each feather was in place. Roger saved his money so that he could travel to the city to see his painting on exhibit.

At the bird club exhibit, a man was introduced to Roger. It was Louis Agassiz Fuertes, the same man who painted those first beautiful birds that Roger copied in the seventh grade. Louis gave Roger some pointers on how to create a feeling of light in his painting of the kingbird. Then he reached into his pocket and pulled out a sable paintbrush. He gave the paintbrush to Roger and told him to send him some of his paintings. Roger treasured the paintbrush and had planned to send his new friend some of his paintings. Less than two years later, Louis Agassiz Fuertes was killed in an accident at a railroad crossing.

Roger Tory Peterson went on to become one of America's finest nature painters. His book, *A Field Guide to the Birds,* was published in 1934 and is still popular among bird-watchers everywhere. He said, "People have begun to see that life itself is important–not just people, but all life. The older I get the more I feel the interconnectedness of things all over the world."

The sable paintbrush that Louis Agassiz Fuertes gave to Roger is now long gone. It fell between some floorboards in his house. Later, when he pulled up the floorboards, he discovered that a mouse had used the bristles to make a nest. He remembered with a smile that this was one of his first lessons on "how everything in life is interconnected."

GA1460

Roger Tory Peterson Activities
Bird-Watching

Bird-watching is one of the fastest growing outdoor activities in North America. All over the country, people are getting interested in all kinds of birds, from the common house sparrow to the regal bald eagle. Bird-watchers of all ages and from all walks of life take part in the hobby.

The North American continent makes up 17 percent of the world's land mass. Of the 8,600 bird species found in the world, there are only about 645 species of birds found in North America. The reason is that North America has no true tropical habitats, where the largest numbers of different species are found.

Some bird-watchers list the names of each species they find, while others just enjoy sitting back and watching the behaviors of birds. Roger Tory Peterson, the ornithologist and artist, just enjoys taking walks and photographing the birds he sees. He uses common bird-watching techniques to get the very best pictures.

Bird-Watching Tips

Be very quiet to observe the natural behavior of birds.

Watch where you are walking. Stay on pathways. Trampling marshes and grasslands may damage or disturb nesting areas.

More experienced bird-watchers can help beginning birders get started.

Leave areas clean from litter.

Getting too close to a nest may cause the parents to abandon their nest or leave the nest open to predators.

Avoid handling eggs or young birds.

Take the time to observe even the most common birds in your area. Look for similarities and differences in markings and behavior. Record what you see.

Keep a journal of the different kinds of birds you see in your area. You don't have to know the names of them. Just write down their markings, what they were doing and where you found them. Bring your findings to school and see if you can name them with the help of books from your school library.

GA1460

Roger Tory Peterson Activities
North American Bird Word Search

```
R  E  V  O  L  P  Q  U  S  H
B  O  S  U  T  J  A  Y  P  U
P  W  A  S  G  G  E  J  A  M
N  L  E  D  N  K  U  L  R  M
O  N  I  E  R  Y  Q  R  R  I
E  L  R  U  D  U  C  K  O  N
G  W  T  E  A  R  N  O  W  G
I  Y  Y  I  S  W  A  N  C  B
P  E  L  I  C  A  N  W  E  I
S  G  N  I  W  L  L  U  G  R
W  B  L  A  C  K  B  I  R  D
E  S  O  O  G  N  O  R  E  H
B  U  G  S  O  L  I  A  T  C
Q  B  E  A  K  W  A  H  A  T
```

egret	pelican	roadrunner	turkey	goose
heron	gull	jay	quail	plover
pigeon	swan	duck	owl	hummingbird
hawk	sparrow	wren	blackbird	beak
bugs	wings	tail	nest	egg

Civilian Conservation Corps: The Soil Soldiers
A Letter Home

May 6, 1934

Dear Mary,

This is my first letter I am writing to you as a "soil soldier." That's right. They call us soil soldiers because we are like an army that is helping the land. I'm sorry that I haven't written to you sooner. Our days begin at six o'clock in the morning and don't end until after our study classes at night. I am pretty tired at the end of the day, but I feel good about the work that we're getting done here for the country.

We all live in a camp, army style. From our barracks you can see the sun come up over the mountains in the morning. It reminds me of the times you and I used to get up real early and sit on the porch swing and watch the sun rise. But now I don't have much time for porch swings.

Last week we had an emergency. A forest fire was heading to town. We dug trenches and pumped water from a creek all night to stop it. Most days though, we find ourselves working on jobs like planting grasses to prevent erosion, drilling wells and building fences. We learn how to use hand tools like pick axes, shovels and crosscut saws. Some of us run heavy machinery like tractors and bulldozers. Next week, we'll be learning about rotating crops and other farm methods. Maybe I'll give farming a try when I come back home.

The first few days, I wasn't sure if this was the right place for me. It was real hard getting used to the different food, the hard work and the study classes at night. Things got better when I started making new friends. It seems as if there is someone from every part of the South right here in our own barracks. I have friends from South Carolina, Mississippi and Georgia. On the weekends we play baseball or go swimming. I met this one guy from Virginia last week. His name is Charles. He misses his family too.

Well, I hope that everything is going all right at home. I know these are tough times. Here is what I saved from my first paycheck. It's not much, but I hope it helps.

Your brother,

Jimmy

GA1460

The Soil Soldiers Activities
Answering the Call to Environmentalism

In the 1930s, the United States was in the middle of the Great Depression. President Roosevelt and his advisors came up with a plan to help bring money to families and do some good for the environment at the same time. The result was a government program called the Civilian Conservation Corps.

Also known as "soil soldiers," the men lived in barracks, worked full eight-hour days and took conservation classes at night. Some learned new skills like how to use hand tools, others learned about constructing buildings, and still others learned how to read and write in their study classes. To these men from all different backgrounds, the nation owes a debt of gratitude.

The Civilian Conservation Corps started in 1934. By the time the program ended in 1942, more than three million men had become soil soldiers.

✉ The letter from Jimmy is fiction. Write a letter to Jimmy as his friend or relative. Use facts from the 1930s. Remember, this was during the Great Depression when people across the nation were out of work and experiencing severe hardship.

Find out what the soil soldiers did in your part of the country.

🌲 What projects might help to improve the area where you are now? Write down your ideas and draw up some plans.

🌲🌲 Think of ways that you and your friends might get together and tackle the project.

The Soil Soldiers
Nine Areas of the Civilian Conservation Corps

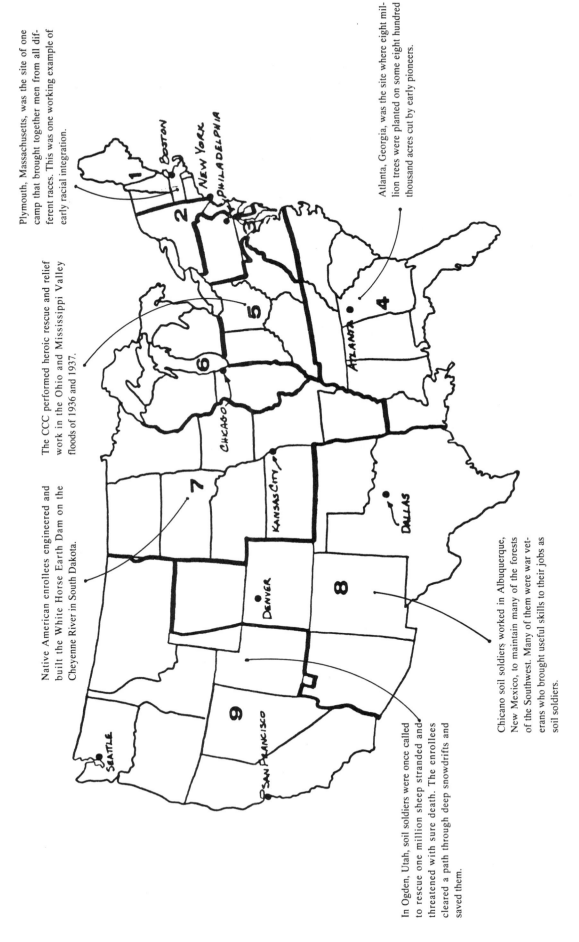

Plymouth, Massachusetts, was the site of one camp that brought together men from all different races. This was one working example of early racial integration.

Atlanta, Georgia, was the site where eight million trees were planted on some eight hundred thousand acres cut by early pioneers.

The CCC performed heroic rescue and relief work in the Ohio and Mississippi Valley floods of 1936 and 1937.

Native American enrollees engineered and built the White Horse Earth Dam on the Cheyenne River in South Dakota.

Chicano soil soldiers worked in Albuquerque, New Mexico, to maintain many of the forests of the Southwest. Many of them were war veterans who brought useful skills to their jobs as soil soldiers.

In Ogden, Utah, soil soldiers were once called to rescue one million sheep stranded and threatened with sure death. The enrollees cleared a path through deep snowdrifts and saved them.

GA1460

William O. Douglas
An Advocate for the Earth

Should natural objects like rocks, streams and mountains have legal rights? William O. Douglas thought so, and he spent most of his life defending those rights.

William O. Douglas was born in 1898 in the state of Washington. Three years later he became ill from polio. The disease left his legs thin and numb. Each day his mother helped him to exercise his leg muscles. The children at school would make fun of him. After a while, he was able to walk with the help of leg braces. William would take regular walks in the mountains near Mount Rainier. His legs became stronger and stronger. He was soon running through the woods.

In 1939, William was appointed to the Supreme Court. His experience in law and working with President Roosevelt in government service would now take a new turn. His new position in Washington, D.C., would give him an opportunity to take a stand for conservation like never before. He was called "The Justice."

The wilderness was a part of William's life. He enjoyed trail riding in the Cascades and loved the feel of the warm Chinook wind on his face. He wrote many books, including *The Wilderness Bill of Rights* and *The Vanishing Wilderness*. Wearing worn boots and a cowboy hat, he joined fellow conservationists as they marched outside Washington, D.C., to stop the building of a freeway on the site of an old canal.

Justice Douglas firmly believed that valleys, meadows, swamps, lakes, beaches and even air had a legal right to exist. He also stated that people like fishers, loggers, biologists and others who enjoy or work in the outdoors have a moral obligation to protect the environment. This obligation would be to speak for

nature and to alert people to threats to nature. William O. Douglas was known as a defender of our nation's natural heritage.

GA1460

William O. Douglas
Vandalism in Our National Parks

This year, more than 250 million people will plan to visit a park in the United States. There are 357 national park units across the country. Some parks, like Fort Scott National Historic Site in Kansas–a recruiting site for African American soldiers during the Civil War, help us to remember an event in history. Parks like Petroglyph National Monument in New Mexico give us a chance to study our country's past. Yellowstone National Park was established to simply preserve the wilderness. All of the parks are protected by laws to make sure that they will be around for future generations to enjoy.

Many of those 250 million people will be disappointed by what they find or don't find when they visit our parks this year. Damage and loss from vandalism and looting are at the root of the problem. At Petroglyph National Monument, rock walls covered with animal and human figures drawn by Native Americans thousands of years ago have been the target of vandals who have shot and spray painted the pictures. At Yellowstone National Park, geysers have been filled with trash and sealed with rocks, and many Civil War battlefields have had problems with looters and grave robbers.

The biggest problem with protecting the more than 80 million acres of national park land is having enough money to hire rangers and other staff to enforce the laws against vandalism. In Canyonlands Park in southern Utah, park rangers talk with the public to educate them about the importance of preserving the park. Backpackers, hikers and other visitors learn to appreciate the landscape and are then less likely to destroy it.

In 1990 there were 10,920 cases of damage to national parks reported to the FBI.

29

GA1460

William O. Douglas Activities
Vandalism

The trail to the caverns was steep. Todd and the rest of his class had waited all year to take this trip. Sarah and Janisa caught up with him at the head of the trail.

"Hey, Todd. Wait up!" said Janisa. "What's your hurry?"

"I want to get to the cave," he said, and then pulled a red handled flashlight from his pocket. "I have to see something."

"What?" said Sarah as they walked up to the mouth of the cave.

"It's a design made by the stalactites in the cavern. They're over 46,000 years old. My brother told me that if you look carefully, you can see the oldest stalactites toward the back of the cavern, but you need a special flashlight like this one." Todd twisted the flashlight and the light narrowed with each turn until it looked like a thin laser beam. He shut it off so he wouldn't use up his batteries.

"Cool," said Janisa.

They were far ahead of the rest of the group as they entered the small cavern. They couldn't wait to see the giant stalactites and stalagmites, formed by mineral deposits and water, hanging from the ceiling and shooting up from the floor like giant teeth. Each year Mrs. Lee's class made this trip. Todd's brother, who was five years older than he was, had even made the trip with Mrs. Lee.

Todd turned on his flashlight. The rest of the class followed. Their feet crunched on something as they walked into the room of the cavern where the old giant was. Todd shone his flashlight on the floor and then up on the walls. Pieces of stalactites and stalagmites were all over the floor. Mrs. Lee held up her lantern near the old giant. The room was flooded with light and shadows as the flame from the lantern hit the tiny crystallized shards.

Someone had taken a bat and shattered the ancient formations, including the old giant. Todd turned and walked out. No one said a word. After everyone had left the cavern, Mrs. Lee called a group meeting.

Does this cavern have any "legal rights" according to William O. Douglas?

If you agree, write down three reasons for those rights.
If you disagree, write down three reasons against those rights.

Organize into small groups and discuss your answers.

GA1460

Rachel Carson and Shirley Briggs

Friends for Life

Rachel Carson and Shirley Briggs were two good friends who shared an interest in science and a commitment to ecology. At the end of World War II, Rachel and Shirley met when they were among the first professional women to be employed by the Department of Fish and Wildlife in Washington, D.C. Rachel was hired as a writer and Shirley as an artist. By working together, they soon found that they shared a common background and many of the same interests. Both Rachel and Shirley were of Scottish-Irish heritage, enjoyed the outdoors and loved bird-watching.

Part of Rachel's job was to take scientific studies of the environment and make them into easy-to-understand reports for the general public. It was through this work that Rachel found out about the harmful effects of chemical pesticides to people and the environment.

Shirley remembers, "Rachel was concerned. She knew that people across the country were using pesticides in their homes and gardens, believing that they were harmless." Rachel worked late into the night and on weekends trying to study how chemical pesticides like

Rachel Carson

DDT would make their way through the food chain and disrupt nature's system of ecology. After four years of careful research, Rachel alerted the world to the dangers of misusing chemical pesticides in her 1964 book, *Silent Spring*.

After a yearlong illness, Rachel Carson died in 1964. Rachel had become known as the "mother of the environmental movement." The public had paid close attention when she spoke out or wrote about the connection between people and nature. Shirley and some of Rachel's closest friends were called together. They were told that Rachel's last wish was that her work continue. She had wanted her friends to keep educating the public about the misuse and abuse of chemical pesticides. A few months later, Rachel's friends established the Rachel Carson Council in Maryland.

Today, Shirley Briggs is still a part of that council. She tells the public about the effects of household chemicals and pesticides on the environment. She talks about having hope for the future. She says, "For years, we were the only ones who would answer questions, but now we have some company." Shirley Briggs and Rachel Carson were the best of friends. Their friendship is still very much alive at the Rachel Carson Council.

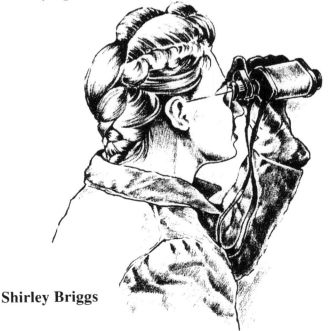

Shirley Briggs

GA1460

Rachel Carson Activities
Pesticides

Pesticide literally means "insect poison." All pesticides are designed to kill or repel insects. There are many kinds of pesticides. Some are made from natural products like ashes, while others are man-made.

In 1987, the Federal Drug Administration detected pesticides in 50 percent of all fruits and 41 percent of all vegetables sampled. What can consumers do to keep down levels of toxins? Washing fruits and vegetables thoroughly before cooking or eating is a start. The real answer is in getting people to try to use other forms of pest management instead of reaching for the spray can every time they see a bug.

Most insects are often harmless or can be repelled with simple solutions. If you have ants in your house, you can find the spot where they are entering and place some honey a short distance away. When the ants have been rerouted to the honey, you can close off the area where they entered the house.

Pesticides can be absorbed into the human body by contact with skin, breathing them into your lungs, or by mouth. All of the health effects of pesticides are not yet known. The effects include skin rashes, breathing problems, eye irritation, birth defects and some types of cancers.

Farm workers, in particular, are at a greater risk for health problems when they work in fields that have been exposed to chemical pesticides.

Organic fruit and vegetables are produced without toxic pesticides.

Integrated Pest Management or IPM involves some use of pesticides in addition to using other techniques to control pests and disease. One method is to introduce the pests' natural enemies. For example, a farmer might introduce ladybugs into a field infested with aphids.

Caution needs to be taken with pesticides used around the house and garden. Many ads and commercials treat the subject of getting rid of bugs by using humor. In reality, these pesticides are as harmful as any misused or abused chemical.

More than twenty years ago Cesar Chávez and the United Farm Workers organized a boycott of table grapes. They helped to stop the use of DDT in table grape vineyards.

Interview

Think about the use of toxic pesticides and their impact on the environment. Write down what you know about pesticides.

Do you know anyone who likes to work with plants, farms or gardens? Ask people you know who work with plants what they think about using pesticides. How do they control pests? Write down their ideas.

Read your ideas and those of the people you interviewed. Have you changed any of your ideas? What answers did the other students in your class get?

Survey

Collect all of the answers from everyone in the class. Chart the information that the class received from their interviews. You can chart whether people used pesticides all the time, some of the time or not at all. You can chart what other methods people used to control pests.

Refer to the Decoding Key on page vi to help you solve the puzzle below.

___ ___   ___ ___ ___ ___ ___ ___ ___   ___ ___ ___ ___

___ ___ ___ ___ ___ ___ ___ ___ ___ ___ .

Barry Commoner
Every Day Is Earth Day

Barry Commoner has been called the "Paul Revere of ecology." In the 1960s he began alerting the public about the dangers of pollution and other problems with the environment. Barry believed that there were many ways that people could work together to find answers to these problems. One of the ways he helped to bring people together was by helping to organize the very first Earth Day.

Barry Commoner was born in 1917. He grew up in Brooklyn, New York. His parents were Russian immigrants who earned their living as tailors. He lived with his parents and his aunt and uncle at the edge of town.

During the day, Barry could usually be found exploring a swamp that led to nearby Jamaica Bay, watching the construction of an elevated railway or visiting the neighbor's goat farm. In the evenings, Barry would teach his mother English, and she would read him stories in Yiddish. Most of his weekends were spent collecting specimens to study from Brooklyn's Prospect Park. Later in life, Barry would find that these early learning experiences helped him to better understand people and ecology.

In 1965, Barry organized a group of scientists to investigate environmental problems. The city of Decatur, Illinois, was one of the first to seek the help of Barry's group. It seemed that the city had discovered high levels of nitrates in the drinking water. Nitrates in different forms can be toxic to people. After studying the region, the group found that since the city was surrounded by farmland, the nitrates were coming from the farmers' fields. By trying to get their plants to produce more, the farmers added more inorganic fertilizer than the plants could use. The extra nitrogen in the fertilizer drained into the rivers and local drinking water supplies. Barry's group helped to identify the problem, and the city worked out its own ways to make sure the community had clean drinking water and the farmers could still produce their crops.

Barry Commoner was not afraid to speak out about his concerns for the health and welfare of our world. He was one of the first people to warn of dangerous atmospheric testing of nuclear weapons in the 1950s. He supported Rachel Carson and other environmentalists in their efforts to alert the nation to the importance of safe ecological practices. He even ran for President of the United States. Today, Barry is still very active at his Center for the Biology of Natural Systems at Queens College in New York.

GA1460

Barry Commoner Activities
Earth Day

Barry Commoner was one of the people who helped to organize the first Earth Day. Try some of these activities and make every day Earth Day!

Role Play

What do you think that first meeting to organize Earth Day was like? Re-create what you think was talked about that day.

What does the phrase "make every day Earth Day" mean? Make a list of some of those things that we can do to make every day Earth Day. Select one or two of those ideas on the list and use them.

Create an environmental cartoon for Earth Day.

GA1460

Jacques Cousteau
A Peaceful Quest

Jacques Cousteau is known for being an explorer, humanitarian, inventor, ecologist, and the list goes on. He co-invented the Aqualung™, an early method for diving underwater. He started the science of undersea archaeology and has always been a defender of nature. His interest in the ocean started at a very young age.

Jean Jacques Cousteau was born more than seventy-five years ago in France. Water fascinated the small boy of four. He loved to touch the water and discover the properties of it with experiments. He tested what things floated and what things sank in water. First he tried toy boats, next his own body, and then stones.

He learned to dive when his family spent some time living in the United States. At the age of ten, his parents sent him to a summer school in Lake Harvey, Vermont. One of his instructors didn't like him, and he didn't like his instructor. The instructor made him ride horses, and the young Jacques fell a lot. One day, the instructor made him clear the bottom of a shallow lake where everyone practiced diving off a springboard. Jacques dove in and pulled out the branches that were stuck in the mud beneath the springboard. That is how he learned to dive and become a good swimmer. Back in France, years later, he tried to practice breathing underwater with a pipe. Jacques dreamed of machines that would permit him to stay and observe underwater.

That was just the beginning. Jacques went on to invent hundreds of tools for underwater research, filming and exploration. He created a special compact submarine for scientific experiments and invented the first underwater television system.

Jacques Cousteau is a peaceful man who believes that we must learn to cherish our fellow human beings for the sake of the environment and ourselves.

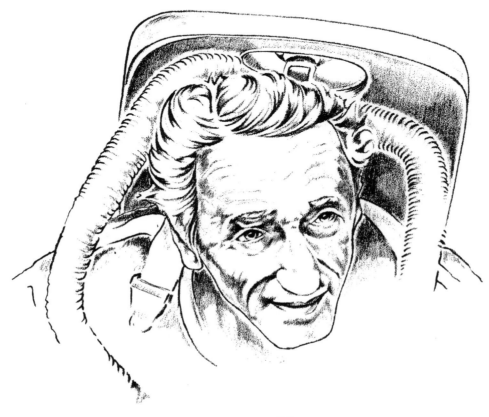

GA1460

Jacques Cousteau Activities

Jean Michel Cousteau, the son of Jacques Cousteau, describes his father as someone who tells us about the future, the many connections between life and hope. His words best describe his understanding of the world and the person who is Jacques Cousteau.

Not only have we failed to realize that we are one people, but we have forgotten that we have only one planet.

The technology that we use to abuse the planet is the same technology that can help us to heal.

The only solution is to require by law the polluters to keep all toxic products within their own fences. This is the only attitude to clean the world.

Select one of the above quotes from Jacques Cousteau. What are his words telling us? What do his words mean in your life? Write your ideas down and then share them with a partner. Listen carefully to what they have to say.

Sub Search

Across:
1. Cousteau ship
4. Narrow bodies of water
7. Water things
8. Together
10. Small, furry sea mammal
12. Type of fish
15. Way to move in water
17. Opposite of young
18. Big Lake in Russia
19. Swedish girl's name
21. Cares for people
23. Country in southern Arabia
25. Wind direction (abbr.)
26. Cousteau's first language
28. Night bird
29. Opposite "from"
30. Famous Pharaoh (abbr.)
31. African country
33. Below
34. Big snake
35. Either . . .

Down:
1. Short for California
2. Latin for water
3. She . . . on a chair
4. Underwater ship
5. City in Brazil (abbr.)
6. Able to get
9. Sea robbers
11. City in Saudi Arabia
12. Partnership (slang)
13. Italian of the past
14. Our world
16. Wet element
20. Dog does it
22. Hurt
24. Lion does it
27. Cable News Network (abbr.)
32. Opposite of "stay"

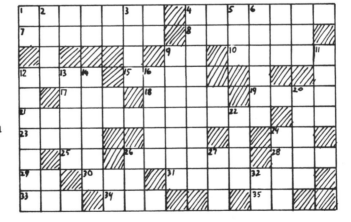

GA1460

Environmental Time Line
Late Twentieth Century

1970   The first Earth Day is held on April 22.

1970   The National Environmental Policy Act is passed. Large federal government construction projects such as dams and highways are now required to first report on how the structure will impact on the environment.

1970   The Clean Air Act gets tough on pollution.

1972   The chemical pesticide DDT is outlawed.

1972   Clean Water Act is passed with the hope of cleaning up polluted waters once used for recreation.

1972   The United States is one of 113 nations represented at a UN Conference meeting in Stockholm to create a plan to protect the world environment.

1972   The first bottle recycling law is passed in Oregon.

1973   The Endangered Species Act is passed to protect living things as well as the environment.

1976   Chlorofluorocarbons used in spray cans and refrigerators are found to be damaging to the ozone layer.

1978   The residents of Love Canal, New York, are evacuated after a toxic dump site is discovered buried under their community.

1981   Canada notifies the United States that 60 percent of the sulfur dioxide air and water pollution in Quebec is due to U.S. industry.

1987   The United States joins other nations in signing an agreement to protect the ozone layer.

1987   Sam LaBudde's videotape of dolphins caught in gillnets brings attention to illegal fishing practices around the world.

1989   *Exxon Valdez* spills more than 11 million gallons of oil in Prince William Sound, Alaska.

GA1460

1989   Mark Wellman and Mike Corbett climb El Capitan, the highest sheer face granite rock in the United States.

1990   Congress bans offshore oil drilling in California, Alaska and the East Coast. More than 84 million acres are protected under this law.

1990   Kevin Bell tests the water at the Stillwater Wildlife Refuge in Nevada and discovers toxic residues from pesticides. His findings helped to pass the Reid Water Bill.

1991   The government redefines the term "wetland." One million of the 100 million acres of protected wetland areas are now open to development.

1991   Carl Anthony, president of Earth Island Institute in San Francisco, helps to organize the first Eco Rap Contest.

1992   The Monterey Bay National Marine Sanctuary is designated in September. Covering areas north of San Francisco to San Luis Obispo, it becomes the largest marine sanctuary in the United States.

GA1460

David Brower
Making His Own Way

David Brower has been called one of the most important environmental activists in the United States. Born and raised in the Berkeley Hills of California, David learned a lot about the environment by exploring his own backyard. In fact, he learned one of the most important lessons in life by raising butterflies at home.

David thought the Western swallowtail butterfly was one of the most beautiful insects in the world. He often watched their bold yellow and black colored wings floating in the gardens and fields near his home. One day, he decided to raise some swallowtails on his own.

He started by collecting clusters of swallowtail eggs. Soon, tiny caterpillars came out of the eggs. At first, they were black with a yellow stripe across the middle, and then later, they turned green with bands of yellow and black.

David fed them carefully, making sure that the tiny creatures had plenty of wild anise and parsley to eat. David watched closely as they found hiding places and began weaving silk thread. Moving onto the silken strands, the caterpillars then shed their skins to form tan-colored chrysalides.

The day that David had waited for had finally come. The chrysalides were dark now and he could see the insects moving inside. First one and then another cracked open. David could not wait. He decided to help free the insects. Gently, he split open the cracks even further so that the butterflies could find their way out easily. He realized too late that this was a mistake. With their wings still folded and their bodies not yet developed, they died within a few minutes.

David did not understand that there was a reason for the butterflies to come out in their own way. By struggling to break free of the chrysalis, the butterfly moves fluid from its abdomen into its folded wings. The fluid is pumped into the veins of the wings to help them expand. After about half an hour, the butterfly tests its wings and is ready to fly. David felt bad about what happened when he tried to free the butterflies, but from this he learned a very important lesson.

As an adult, David used this valuable lesson in his daily life and work in the environmental movement. In his leadership with such organizations as the Sierra Club and Friends of the Earth, David tried to make sure that even the smallest of creatures had a place to make its own way.

Brower, David: *For Earth's Sake: The Life and Times of David Brower,* Gibbs, Smith Publisher, Salt Lake City Utah, 1990.

GA1460

David Brower Activities
Letting Things Fly

Butterflies and other insects interested David Brower. He learned many lessons in life from watching them. Write about one of the topics below or create your own idea!

Describe a time when you watched an insect very closely. Where were you? What did it look like? What was it doing? What did you find out?

Make up a story about an insect. Try to write from the insect's point of view.

What do you think about the practice of collecting and mounting insects? Do you agree or disagree? Support your opinions with examples from your life experience.

What do you think David Brower learned from releasing the butterflies too early from their chrysalides? Describe a similar experience you or someone you know may have had.

Refer to the Decoding Key on page vi to help you solve the puzzle below.

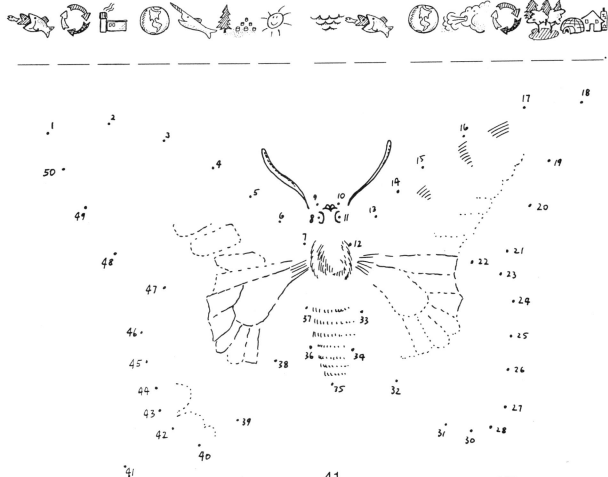

41

GA1460

Andy Lipkis
Trees for a City

Here in the United States, in our city, you and I can change the way we treat the environment. You and I can make a long-term difference as we seek to save our planet earth....

When fifteen-year-old Andy Lipkis went to summer camp in the San Bernadino Mountains near Los Angeles, he never expected that his idea for a camp project would turn into a lifetime career. It all started one evening when a naturalist came to speak to the campers about the local mountains and forests.

The naturalist told the campers that smog was destroying many of the trees in the area. Andy asked if anything could be done to solve the problem. The naturalist replied that there were a few types of trees that could grow even in smog. These trees were known as smog-tolerant trees. Andy asked why the dead trees couldn't be replaced with smog-tolerant ones. The naturalist simply answered that it would be nearly impossible to replant an entire forest.

Fifteen-year-old Andy looked into the valley below him and watched the hazy brown smog creeping toward the mountains. He decided to talk the problem over with his friends as they sat around the campfire that evening. The group came up with an idea to plant some smog-tolerant trees around their campground.

With permission from their counselors, the campers dug up an old parking lot and planted twenty Coulter pine and incense cedar seedlings. Andy felt good about the project. He believed that these new trees would be more resistant to the effects of smog and would bring new growth into the forest.

Andy went on to college to study the environment. When he was in school, he learned how air pollution can damage the way a tree processes its food. He also found out how trees can actually help to filter pollutants from the air and produce oxygen. Andy then started to wonder—if planting trees in the mountains works, then why not plant them in cities as well?

In 1973, Andy founded the organization TreePeople. The group has since helped to plant more than one million trees in the Los Angeles area and educate school and community groups about recycling and other ways to help the environment.

Andy Lipkis started out with an idea and a handful of trees, and like those trees, his ideas have helped to branch out and bring new life to our world.

GA1460

Andy Lipkis Activities
The Value of Trees

The value of trees is often overlooked or taken for granted. Most of us know that people, animals and insects use trees for food and shelter, but did you know that trees play an important role in influencing the weather? From the paper we write on to the air we breathe, trees not only make our lives more pleasant but possible.

Forests regulate the climate and influence weather patterns.

All parts of trees support colonies of plants, animals, birds and insects.

The root systems of trees help to hold topsoil in place, prevent erosion and channel water.

```
S M O G T O L E R A N T Z
T R I D E E R T O O C T B
C C E D A R Z E O I E S A
E N L I O S P O T C R E R
S O L I A N D Y S L R R K
N I I N M S R A I R I O B
I S O O N A E L C T A F E
C O S T N A T U L L O P E
A R L E A F A E N I P E T
N E G Y X O W B I R D S L
C A R B O N D I O X I D E
```

roots	topsoil	climate
insects	filter	pollutants
water	tree	oxygen
erosion	forest	carbon dioxide
leaf	dirt	bark beetle
soil	pine	cedar
air	city	Andy
clean	birds	smog tolerant

GA1460

Take a look around your classroom and make a list of all the products made from trees. Write down ways to conserve, recycle or reuse each product.

It takes seventeen trees to make one ton of paper.

Ways to Conserve, Recycle or Reuse
1. Share a newspaper with a group of friends.
2. Collect newspapers and take them to a recycling center.
3. Reuse old newspapers for art projects like papier-mâché or for drop cloths for messy activities.

In Los Angeles County alone, over 5000 tons of paper are thrown away each day.

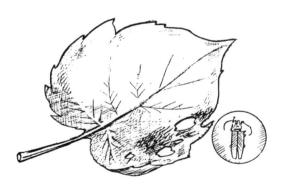

Some trees are more smog tolerant than others. Smog can destroy a tree's ability to produce food for itself. The tree weakens and then is open to attack by insects like bark beetles.

Trees are important to people in many ways. In the fields of science and medicine, tree products can be used to make fuel more efficient or as a source of a lifesaving cancer treatment.

Carbon dioxide (CO_2) is a colorless and odorless gas found in nature. Products such as coal, oil and wood release carbon dioxide when they are burned. Large amounts of gases like carbon dioxide are released into the atmosphere and create worldwide changes in climate and sea levels (greenhouse effect).

GA1460

Mark Wellman
A Climb to Remember

At thirty-six hundred feet, El Capitan in Yosemite National Park is the highest sheer face granite rock in the United States, and Mark Wellman wanted to climb it. Mark got the help of Mike Corbett, an experienced rock climber, to make the climb. Mike had climbed the rock more than forty times and was known as "Mr. El Cap." Mark knew that he would make the best climbing partner for this adventure.

July 19, 1989, the day of the climb arrived. Six months of planning and training had gone into getting ready for this day. Mark pulled on the rock chaps he had designed to protect his legs from the hard granite surface of El Capitan. Carefully, he checked his gear to make sure that everything was in place. He hooked his pull-up bar to the ropes hanging from the face of the rock. He was ready to go.

In one strong move, he began to pull himself up "the big wall." With each pull-up Mark gained about half a foot in distance. Mike climbed ahead of Mark setting the ropes into place. As the morning wore on, the granite became warm from the summer sun. At the end of the first day, the pair had reached Mammoth Terrace, a small ledge. They had just enough time to rest and eat before sunset. After more than two thousand pull-ups that day, Mark was glad to get some sleep. His climbing adventure had just begun.

Each day brought something new to the climbers. One day Mike got stuck in a crack as he climbed with a pack on his back. On another day, the two found themselves climbing along the bottom of an overhang with twenty-five hundred feet of air below them. Tired and worn as they crawled along the hot rock, the two had to ration their water toward the end of the climb. Mark and Mike could now see a crowd of newspaper and television reporters on the summit. The last night, they

knew they were near the end and enjoyed telling each other jokes and stories.

The final few feet of the climb, Mike carried Mark on his back. Mike's foot began to slip and Mark remembered the climbing accident that left him paralyzed below the waist. Mike got his footing again and came up over another section of rocks and the two were welcomed by cheering reporters, park officials and friends. After more than seven thousand pull-ups it was time to celebrate.

GA1460

An Interview with Mark Wellman
Outdoor Adventurer

In 1982, Mark Wellman was injured in a serious climbing accident in the Sierra Nevada mountains. He became paralyzed below the waist and lost the use of both legs. Just a few years later, the eyes of the country were on Mark and his climbing partner Mike Corbett as they scessfully completed a 13-day climb up the face of Yosemite's Half-Dome.

How would you describe yourself?

I see myself as someone who is at the leading edge of outdoor sports and pushing the limits. I enjoy skiing, climbing, kayaking and horseback riding. I'm an outdoor adventurer. Outdoor adventure is my business these days. I have a business called No Limits. I talk to people at hospitals, schools and companies and show them videotapes of my work. I also adapt and test sports equipment for the disabled.

What project are you working on now?

I'm also getting ready to ski across the Sierra Nevada next winter. It's my next big challenge. I'm on the U.S. Disabled Ski Team. We're going to go through Yosemite on the Tioga Pass Road. It's a fifty-mile cross country ski trip going over a 10,000 foot pass.

The big difference between this adventure and my climbing adventure is that this one will be without able-bodied assistance. It will be myself and another person who is a paraplegic.

What are some ways people with disabilities can enjoy the wilderness?

The disabled can enter the wilderness by adapting equipment to their own needs. For example, you can adapt a saddle to ride stock horses or mules into the back country if you can't walk in on your own legs. You can also use an adaptive wheelchair that uses mountain bike tires to go over rugged ground. Everyone who goes into the wilderness has to be prepared for dealing with the outdoors. You have to be responsible by bringing your own shelter in and taking your garbage out.

What is important for people to know about the environment in this country?

Our forefathers in this country set up a pretty good national park system, forestry service and other groups for helping the environment. We need to think about ecology, land preservation and recycling. Those things are definitely a part of my lifestyle.

Mark Wellman Activities
Getting to the Top

There is only one route that will take you from the bottom to the top of this "amazing" mountain. Find your way!

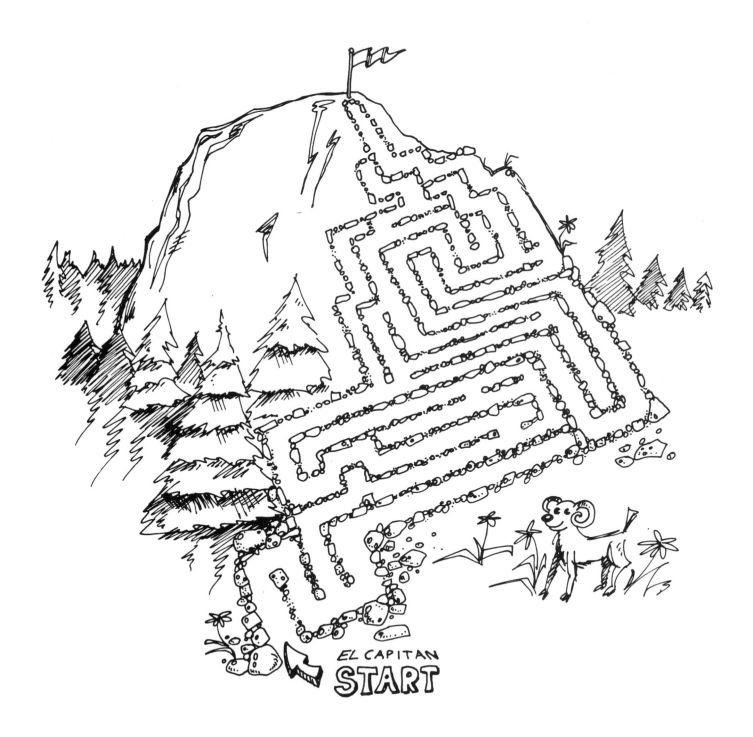

EL CAPITAN
START

Outdoor Sports

There are many different kinds of outdoor sports. What outdoor sports do you enjoy? Skiing, boating, roller blading, hot air ballooning, horseback riding and surfing–the list is endless.

Some involve the challenge of competition while others are simply enjoyed for pleasure. Yet all require safety and instruction in learning important skills. Mark Wellman believes that protective equipment and learning from experienced teachers are two safety factors important in any sport.

Mark Wellman says that in climbing "You are always concentrating on making sure that everything is secure so you don't lose anything. So you really need to make sure your knots are right. It is a very slow and methodical process. Gravity works against you. When you are working on the cliff's surface and you drop something, you just have to say good-bye to it. Gravity can make you fall too."

Lynn Hill is a champion sport climber who has competed in many parts of the world, including Japan, France, Germany and the USA. With little more than a finger hold and a rope, sport climbers spend many hours figuring out precise moves to tackle even the shortest of climbing routes. In a series of dance-like moves, they make their way up the flattest of surfaces. You may find them working their way up smooth natural rocks or man-made concrete slabs. A safety harness helps to keep Lynn from falling too far or getting hurt too seriously.

Jim Goodbar was nine years old when his father gave him a flashlight and took him to explore some caves. Since then, Jim has traveled the world looking into caves, and he's found some very interesting things. In Tennessee, he once found the skeletons of jaguars and Native Americans more than 4000 years old. Whenever Jim goes exploring in caves, he makes sure he has a hard hat with a chin strap, a long sleeved shirt, long pants, and a good pair of boots with plenty of traction. His most important tools are lights and a partner. You can't risk losing either one.

Sheri Griffith is a river outfitter who specializes in bringing people and the environment together. Her expedition company offers white water rafting trips in Utah and Colorado for the whole family. On her trips people of all ages learn about hiking, bouldering, water games and how to have a good time safely. She and her guides are professionals who are well trained in first aid and wilderness medicine. Sheri makes sure that all of the equipment, from the rafts to the life jackets, are in perfect working order.

Scott Carpenter has been an astronaut and lived on the ocean floor for over a month. More than thirty years ago, he became one of the first astronauts in outer space. His explorations underwater led him to spend thirty days on the ocean floor in a Sealab. One of his most interesting discoveries was that people could live and work under the sea or out in space. A big part of safety underwater or in space is making sure you have enough air. Once while underwater, Scott's breathing apparatus stopped working. He managed to get back to the lab before he passed out.

GA1460

Conduct a Survey!

Ask some of the students and staff at your school to name their favorite outdoor sports.

Study your findings. How many people chose water sports? How many chose sports done on the land? How about sports done in the air? Make up your own categories to think and talk about with a partner.

Get a partner and share your findings. How were they the same and how were they different?

Outdoor Sport Word Unscramble

ganyaikk   _____

slaiing   _____

abucs gdviin   _____

crok cglimbni   _____

revir rftaing   _____

kisign   _____

ballnnigoo   _____

gsrufin   _____

gnah ggliidn   _____

mnountai bkinig   _____

gnnnrui   _____

khinig   _____

kcabesroh gnidir   _____

GA1460

Thinking About the Issues

Thinking and talking about the issues related to outdoor adventure sports is important. Select one of the subjects below or think up your own. Share your comments and questions with others in your group.

How might adventure sports like mountain biking affect a park trail? Should mountain bikes be allowed on all park trails?

What are some ways to make the wilderness more accessible to people in wheelchairs? Should we cut new trails into untouched wilderness for people with disabilities?

What are some of the risks involved in outdoor adventure sports? Should there be laws to make sure that people wear protective clothing and equipment, or should each person make his or her own decision? What about kids?

GA1460

Juliana Furtado
Mountain Bike Racer

each bump with her legs. After 1986, Juliana Furtado joined the University of Colorado ski squad, where she perfected her skiing style in the slalom and giant slalom. That was until injuries to her knee turned her to the sport of professional mountain bike racing. In 1990, she won the very first world championship mountain bike race held in Durango.

Juliana has learned a lot about safety and control of mountain bikes since she's been on the racing circuit. She says avoiding a crash has to do with thinking ahead. One of the worst kinds of crashes is when people go head-over the handlebars. Juliana says that by shifting your weight to the back of the saddle and using the front brake lightly, you can avoid many serious mishaps.

Juliana Furtado compares mountain bike racing to downhill skiing, and why not? At 24, she is not only a world champion mountain bike racer, but a member of the U.S. Ski Team. She says that many of the same moves that she used as a skier have helped her with her mountain bike technique.

Charging up hills through mud, dirt and rocks, Juliana banks her bike off the sidehills and gets down really low as she hits a hollow part of the trail. When she goes downhill, she stands up out of the saddle of her bike. "Whack!" Her bike hits a rock in the road. She folds her arms and legs close to her body so that she isn't thrown off balance. Juliana uses the same manuevers in skiing when she goes over moguls. She keeps the upper part of her body steady and absorbs the shock of

51

GA1460

Juliana Furtado Activities
Mountain Bikes and Road Bikes: What's the Difference?

What are some of the differences between road bikes and mountain bikes? What do you think are the reasons for some of these differences?

Biking is a great way to see the outdoors and explore your environment.

Bicycles do not create air pollution.

Biking on a regular basis can help to keep you physically fit.

What are some other reasons for biking?

Bicycle Safety

- Know when to brake. Braking too fast could cause a serious spill.

- Look ahead. The faster you go the more important it is to keep your eyes on where you are going. You can anticipate things like strategies for maneuvering between obstacles.

- Try standing on the pedals for more power. By standing on the pedals and moving from side to side, you can put all your weight on the pedals.

- Get off and walk your bike through especially tough areas like sand.

- Maintain your balance over obstacles like rocks or ruts. Ease your body up and over by relaxing your upper body and keeping a loose grip on the handlebars.

- Follow safety rules and wear protective gear and clothing. Use protective glasses, gloves, and front and rear lights for riding in the city.

Juliana Furtado Activities
Bicycle Terms Word Search

```
H   A   N   D   L   E   B   A   R   S
N   I   E   S   F   R   A   M   E   A
I   N   I   K   A   O   I   U   C   D
A   C   E   K   O   L   O   D   H   D
T   L   E   N   E   P   E   D   A   L
N   I   G   E   A   R   S   S   I   E
U   N   G   L   I   A   R   T   N   N
O   E   O   T   E   M   L   E   H   U
M   W   D   N   A   S   R   O   A   D
```

saddle	brake	handlebars	frame
tire	spoke	helmet	chain
mountain	road	trail	sand
mud	incline	mile	pedal
gears			

GA1460

Sheri Griffith
River Outfitter

Your river guide tells you to "hold on" as your raft hits a huge rolling section of ten-foot waves. Soon, your raft is floating along a peaceful stretch of the river, and your guide is telling you about the way Native Americans, cowboys and outlaws used the canyons around you. Stopping on a sandy white beach of the river, your guide shows you how to set up camp with the health of the environment in mind. Your guide's name is Sheri Griffith.

Sheri owns and operates a river outfitting business in Moab, Utah. The name of her business is Sheri Griffith Expeditions. She and her staff of river guides take people for day outings and overnight camping trips along the Colorado and Green Rivers. Each outing is a special mixture of adventure, history and environmental education. Sheri says the river teaches many lessons.

On the river, people learn firsthand how to live with nature. Sheri says you can't force the current to move in the direction that you want it to move. You have to work with the current and understand where you are going. Safety is a priority, and Sheri and the other guides make sure that everyone knows how to respond in different situations. She knows that panic is something that can get people hurt. The motto at Sheri Griffith Expeditions is "take only pictures and leave only footprints." This saying reminds everyone that the canyon is a place to be respected. The company backs up their motto by using recycled products whenever possible and by leaving "no trace of our passage on the water."

Sheri applies what she's learned on the river to her approach in working with environmental problems in many parts of the country. She knows that when people are worried about providing food and shelter for their families, it's not easy for them to think about environmental problems. A lot of people think that you have to make a choice between jobs and the environment. Sheri believes that you don't have to sacrifice one for the other.

Through the years, Sheri has gained a respected reputation as one of the country's leading conservationists. She has been nationally recognized many times over for her work in the areas of recreational resources, business and social service. Sheri Griffith is someone who is comfortable whether she is white water rafting along the Colorado or speaking out for the protection of the wilderness in front of Congress.

Sheri Griffith Activities
White Water Rafting Word Search

```
C  O  N  S  E  R  V  A  T  I  O  N
A  A  O  R  I  D  E  D  I  U  G  C
N  R  I  T  A  O  L  F  P  D  N  I
Y  S  T  A  O  B  R  A  O  I  I  N
O  E  I  F  D  S  D  E  Q  V  T  E
N  R  D  O  D  D  W  A  V  E  F  C
L  U  E  I  L  S  W  I  M  I  A  S
L  T  P  E  K  H  I  S  T  O  R  Y
O  A  X  R  E  T  T  I  F  T  U  O
R  N  E  R  U  T  N  E  V  D  A  Q
```

rafting	river	adventure	expedition	oar
paddle	conservation	guide	outfitter	canyon
boat	scenic	rapids	wave	history
nature	swim	float	ride	oars
roll	dive			

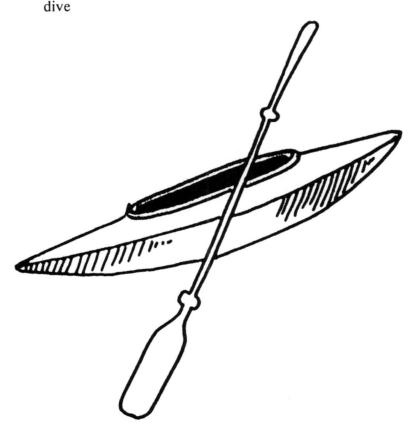

GA1460

Sheri Griffith Activities
White Water Rafting

What's different in these two pictures?

Create White Water Poem

Describe in single words strung together what you might feel like going down a river.

Example:

Calm–soothing–rolling–wave–rapids–bigger–exploding–crashings–wet–wild!

GA1460

Kevin Bell
From the Look of Things

Kevin Bell knows that just because something looks safe doesn't mean that it is safe. A couple of years ago, ten-year-old Kevin read that fish and wildlife were dying at the Stillwater Wildlife Refuge in Nevada near his home. Kevin knew that the refuge was surrounded by thousands of acres of farmland. He thought there might be a connection between pesticides and chemicals used on the farms and the dying wildlife. Kevin went to the refuge with his mom Gailen and decided to investigate the problem.

When he got to the refuge, Kevin obtained a five-gallon sample of water. The water looked perfectly clear. That was the problem. There was no life of any kind in the water. Kevin took the sample and ran some tests at home. He looked around the house and collected some old jars, tubs and other things he would need. His tests involved taking live plants, pond organisms and fish and placing them into the water from the refuge. Kevin found that no living creature he tested could survive in the pond water. He wrote the information down in a wirebound notebook. Kevin took the results from his tests to the state science fair and won first place, and his mom took his findings to the refuge headquarters.

The scientists who had been studying the refuge were amazed. Kevin had found the same results in his study that they had found in their studies. The scientists had spent over $30,000 to get the same results as Kevin. In May of 1990, Kevin's test results were entered into the Congressional Record. His findings were used to help pass the Reid Water Bill. This law helped to close the polluted drain that led to the refuge. New water was introduced into the Stillwater Refuge a few months later, and Kevin was there to celebrate and took part in the ceremony to open the flood gates and bring unpolluted water into the area.

Kevin Bell Activities
Testing the Waters

Fill a glass container with water and place it in front of you.

Describe the properties of water that you can see, smell and touch. Write these properties down.

Experiment with water by seeing what floats and what sinks in your container of water. Write down what happens after each object is placed in the water.

Write down the uses of water that you know about. How do people use water to live, work and play?

Design an experiment with water. Draw your blueprint and write down the steps that you will take. Follow through and conduct your experiment. Share with a friend what worked and what didn't work with your project. Be supportive of what is happening with your friend's experiment as well.

Kevin Bell was recognized for his efforts by President George Bush.

58

GA1460

Carl Anthony
Respect Yourself

First, respect yourself. Every experience you have has a value.

In 1991, Carl Anthony, an urban ecologist, got people interested in a unique way to take action for the environment. Carl is president of the environmental organization Earth Island in San Francisco. His job is to help people in the city take action against the environmental problems happening right in their own neighborhoods. Carl says that low income areas are particularly hard hit by environmental trouble. Often, low income areas are targeted as sites for toxic dumping. There is also less money to spend on clean-up campaigns.

Carl believes that it's important to understand how to make safe environmental changes that work for all groups of people. He says, "One way to make sound environmental changes is to encourage young people to act on the lessons of the environmental movement. We need more environmental leaders from different backgrounds, leaders who can understand the needs of different groups, especially the poor." Carl knows that one of the best ways for people to take action in their own community is by supporting projects that are important to them. That's why he listened closely when he heard the idea for the Eco Rap contest.

The first Eco Rap contest was held in July of 1991. Open to all amateur rappers in San Francisco's bay area, the rules stated that rappers could make a difference for the environment with music. The winners of the contest would go on a "Toxic Tour" of the bay area to help educate people in the city about the dangers of urban pollution. Carl says that the contest helped to let people know that they could do something about the high levels of lead in paint and the ground, air pollution from nearby freeways and factories, and other problems in the city. Eco Rap has become a regular event, and Carl Anthony has helped to get out the word.

GA1460

Carl Anthony Activities
Environmental Poetry

Express yourself!

Make a statement about and for the environment!

Create an Eco Rap or use another form of poetry. Some poems rhyme while others don't, but all are a way to EXPRESS YOURSELF.

Some poems rhyme.

Keeping Things Green
Living on the dark side,
not the light side

Knowing what's right
on the inside

Keeping things green
for the outside

Keeping things green
Keeping things green
Keeping things green!

Some poems have a form you can see.

Other poems have a form you can hear, like the Japanese poetry of haiku. This poem is written by Bill Tao, a strawberry grower who lives in California's Pajaro Valley.

Color of the fire
blazing along the roadside
the Golden Poppies

Other poems are simply free flowing thoughts and feelings . . . .

GA1460

Sam LaBudde
A New Way of Seeing

Have you ever heard of Sam LaBudde? If you haven't, then maybe you know his work. In 1987, Sam hired on as a crew member of a Panamanian tuna boat. For five months he worked on the boat doing odd jobs such as making repairs and cooking. What the owner of the boat did not know was that Sam was a biologist who was videotaping illegal fishing practices.

Sam watched carefully each time the captain gave the order to release yard after yard of deadly gillnets into the ocean. After more than a mile of net was released, the fishermen waited for the tuna to get caught in the finely woven nylon netting. Sam began recording as the net was hauled in. Herds of dolphins were caught. Some were still alive and some had already drowned in the nets. While the tuna were separated out and placed in storage, the live dolphins were slaughtered or left to die on deck and then thrown overboard.

Millions of Americans watched the grisly footage on news programs across the nation. When people saw the real-life pictures of the damage caused by the use of gillnets, they refused to buy tuna. This nationwide boycott forced many tuna companies to change the way they fished. On Thursday, April 12, 1990, Star-Kist™, the largest tuna company in the world, announced that it would stop buying tuna caught in gillnets because of the damage they cause to dolphins and other marine life. They even placed a "dolphin safe" label on their cans. Other tuna companies quickly followed their lead. This was the direct result of Sam's undercover work.

Some people do not agree with Sam's work. Some tuna fishermen in this country say that Sam's videotape put them out of business. They say that using this type of gillnet is the only way they can compete with other fishing boats. Others feel that a boycott is unfair to those fishermen who use legal fishing practices and respect marine life.

Sam LaBudde has been called an "eco-warrior." His undercover work has also revealed illegal fur seal hunting practices in Alaska. Sam LaBudde has done much to prevent the needless slaughter of animals on this earth.

Sam LaBudde Activities
Thinking About the Issues

Some people think that Sam Labudde is helping to make the earth a safer place to live by video-taping inhumane practices, such as the use of gillnets and driftnets.

Others, like some tuna boat fishermen, believe that videotaping and then boycotting tuna were unfair practices that cost many of them their livelihoods.

What do you think? Write down your view. What are some facts to back up your opinion?

Get together with a few students in your class to dialogue your different opinions. Make sure everyone gets a chance to speak.

GA1460

Robin Cannon
One Concerned Citizen

Photo of Juanita Tate and Robin Cannon

Thanks to citizens like Robin Cannon, the community of South Central Los Angeles is breathing a little easier these days. You see, Robin is one of the founding members of the Concerned Citizens of South Central Los Angeles. CCSCLA, as it is called, works to make this district of Los Angeles a cleaner and safer place for people to live, work and visit.

It all started one evening when Robin, a city clerk, came home from work and noticed a pamphlet sticking out of her mailbox. The pamphlet told about a public meeting being held that night by the Bureau of Sanitation. At the meeting, they would announce plans to build a 535 million dollar municipal waste incinerator in South Central Los Angeles. Robin was worried about the effects that a giant waste incinerator would have on her family and community. She decided to go to the meeting and find out more about the project.

The meeting hall was filled with people from the local community and representatives from the city. Robin listened carefully as the officials from the Bureau of Sanitation explained how a waste incineration plant might benefit the area. They explained that the plant would bring new jobs and more money to the residents of the area.

Robin knew that her community could use the new jobs and more money. South Central Los Angeles was an area where people from many different backgrounds lived and worked together. South Central Los Angeles had one of the highest rates of unemployment in the city and new jobs were hard to find. Money raised by the plant could be used to improve school buildings or create programs to reduce crime. Robin waited until everyone had a chance to make a comment or ask questions, then she took her turn to speak.

She was nervous standing up at the microphone, but she felt it was important to get some answers to her questions. She asked about the air pollutants that might be released from the plant. She wanted to know about the routes the garbage trucks would take as they brought waste to the incinerator. She asked so many questions that the city officials gave her their entire report to read. Robin stayed up late that night to go over the report. After she had finished, she not only had more questions, but some new concerns as well.

Robin discovered that the incineration plant would emit fluorines and dioxins, two of the most dangerous poisons known to humans. Zoning changes would threaten the loss of homes, businesses and churches. As she started talking to her friends about her concerns, Robin realized that she was not the only one worried about the incineration project. A few days later, Robin was among a handful of community members meeting to find ways of stopping the project. It was at that meeting that the group Concerned Citizens of South Central Los Angeles was born.

CCSCLA called upon the community to stop the project. Soon they started receiving offers of help. Some offered to collect information from friends and relatives, while others kept community members up to date on the progress of the campaign. Children handed out meeting notices and conducted neighborhood surveys. After more than two years, the group won the campaign to stop the incineration plant.

Today, Robin is still a part of CCSCLA as it continues to work for the health and welfare of the community. The group is active in helping to sponsor food drives and neighborhood cleanups, create affordable housing and much more. Robin believes the campaign did much more than stop a municipal waste incinerator from being built. She says that it brought the community of South Central Los Angeles much closer together. People of many different colors found themselves working together for the same purpose.

Robin remembers, "It all started when some people thought that we wouldn't say anything or know any better to ask questions." Robin Cannon is one concerned citizen, who with the help of others like herself is making the community of South Central Los Angeles a safer place to live.

Robin Cannon Activities
Waste Incineration

The United States is one of the most wasteful countries on earth. Since 1965, the amount of waste we produce each year has increased to more than 150 million tons.

According to the Environmental Protection Agency, Americans seem to waste a lot of paper, glass and plastic. What do you think?

Collect the garbage from your classroom wastebasket each day for a week.

At the end of each day put on protective gloves and separate your garbage into different categories of plastic, paper, glass, etc.

The following week analyze your data. Make a chart of what you found in the garbage can.

Get together with other members of your class to discuss ways of recycling and reusing the garbage you throw away.

Select one or two of these environmental suggestions and put them into practice!

Stephanie Yu
Kids Have Choices

Your choices will, over time, make a difference. Every little thing will affect the world.

Stephanie Yu believes that kids can make a difference in cleaning up and protecting our environment. As the host of the science program *3-2-1 Contact* and other television specials, Stephanie had a lot of opportunities to travel and learn about what was happening with the environment on a firsthand basis. "I'm more aware of what's around me now," she says.

She remembers one of the most exciting experiences she had was going to the rain forest in La Salva, Costa Rica. The rain forest was a big change from New York City. Everything from the insects, plants and even the air was different. She got interested in a Poison Dart Frog. She liked the mixed shading of green and red on its back. She thought to herself, "How can something so cute be so dangerous?"

In her television work, Stephanie has dug around in landfills, reported on the rain forest in Costa Rica, and investigated the way we use the precious resource of water. Yet she knows that there is a difference between talking about and actually doing something for the environment.

"For anybody, it takes time to get accustomed to environmentally sound practices. I tried explaining recycling to my mom. At first, it wasn't easy. Now my mom understands things more. With her generation everything was just so disposable." Stephanie also knows that it's going to take more than recycling to solve the pollution problem, but she feels that every little thing will eventually make a difference.

As a host of *3-2-1 Contact*, Stephanie has not only helped to teach others about the importance of science in our daily lives, but she has also learned to practice it in her own life. Stephanie's work has encouraged many young people across the country to make more responsible and informed choices about the future of our environment.

GA1460

Stephanie Yu Activities
Landfill Waste

Litter can be found almost anywhere in the United States. It washes up on the shores of lakes and beaches. It is dumped by truckloads onto our deserts and can even be found in the most remote areas of the wilderness.

Each year volunteers go out to these areas to clean up millions of tons of trash. What are they finding? On our nation's streets, the list includes fruit peels and cores, cigarette butts, paper, plastic bags, cans and glass bottles. The fruit peels and cores may take as long as two years to decompose, while plastic can take more than a century, if ever, to break down.

Cleanup programs like Adopt-a-Beach have recorded large volumes of boating wastes, fishing line and household trash. It is common in many coastal areas to find birds and other wildlife who have died from getting caught or swallowing litter.

1992 Statistics from the U.S. Environmental Protection Agency:

Create a graph based on the following information about some of the materials produced and recovered from our garbage in 1992.

Material	Amount Generated	Percent Recovered
paper	71.8 million tons	25.6
glass	12.5 million tons	12.0
aluminum	2.5 million tons	31.7
plastics	14.4 million tons	1.1
wood	6.5 million tons	0
rubber and leather	4.6 million tons	2.3

What does this information tell you about the garbage we produce?

What is the total amount of garbage generated by just these seven items?

What materials seem to be most or least often recovered? Why?

Foghorn Newsletter, published by Friends of Gaia, P.O. Box 302, West River, MD 20078.

Miliani Trask
Hawaii Is Her Home

Each year, thousands of people visit the beautiful islands of Hawaii, but for Miliani Trask, Hawaii is her home. Miliani is an attorney and leader of the Ka Lahui Hawaii, a group of native Hawaiian people established in 1987. One of Miliani's goals for the group is to protect the people, the land and the culture of Hawaii.

In 1991, Miliani spoke at a very special environmental conference. This was the first national conference that brought attention to the involvement of people of color in the environmental movement. In the past, native Hawaiians, African Americans, Hispanic Americans, Native Americans, Asian Americans and other groups have not been well represented in many of the large environmental organizations. For many years, Native Americans and other groups have worked hard to solve environmental problems in their own communities. The conference was a way to get different groups to help each other. Miliani's speech gave a voice to the native Hawaiian people.

Her words described the way many people have used the island without care or concern for its natural resources. One of the problems she talked about was the impact of tourism on the islands. Each year, hundreds of thousands of tourists come to Hawaii in search of "paradise." Many natural areas are being turned into resorts or other places for tourists to use. Although tourism brings a lot of money to the islands, she is concerned that the islands cannot sustain the large numbers of tourists that flock to Hawaii.

Another problem is the contamination of the islands' water supplies. "Hawaii is an island ecology," she says. "We do not get fresh water from flowing streams. All the water that falls from the rain in Hawaii is percolated through the lava of the islands. As the rains percolate down they bring with them herbicides and pesticides from large agricultural businesses dealing in pineapple and sugar cane and golf courses."

She says that commitment and energy will be needed to "save our Mother Earth and to insure the survival of our people and all the species of the earth." She says that the conference helped to renew her belief in people and hope for Ka Lahui Hawaii.

GA1460

Miliani Trask Activities
Wao Kele O Puna

Wao Kele O Puna means "green forest on the Puna side." It is the name of the last and largest surviving inland tropical rain forest in the United States. It is home to a host of unique species such as the honey creeper, a bird that helps to pollinate trees. The honey creepers, like many of the plants and animals in this rain forest, are on the endangered species list. The Wao Kele O Puna in many ways represents the heart of the native Hawaiian culture.

Many kahuna, the masters of native Hawaiian culture, use the rain forest to find special herbs for healing. The plants and feathers of birds are also used as a part of the traditional dress in ceremonial dances. Many of these plants can only be found in the Wao Kele O Puna.

People such as Miliani Trask are working to save the last remaining rain forest in the United States from developers. Already, roads plowed into the forest have resulted in plants dying and a disruption of the habitat for wildlife. Developers interested in tapping into the energy located beneath the rain forest are eager to begin drilling. The future of the rain forest is still not decided. Just as we work to save the valuable rain forests in Costa Rica and other parts of the world, we must also save the last remaining one in this country.

The Wao Kele O Puna is located near the active volcano Kilauea. Some native Hawaiians say that the recent volcanic activity is the result of the volcano goddess Pele. They believe that she is angered by the threatened loss of the Wao Kele O Puna.

Wao Kele O Puna is located on the big island of Hawaii. The rain forest is located on some of the largest mountains in the world. Measured from the sea floor to the summit, these mountains combine with a unique island climate to create the perfect conditions for a lowland rain forest. Find out more about the unique geography of Hawaii from your local library.

Make a detailed map of the Big Island. How is it the same or different from where you live?

Find out about other rain forests in the world and how they compare to Wao Kele O Puna.

Miliani Trask Activities

```
C  V  O  L  C  A  N  O  L  I  F  E
E  F  I  L  D  L  I  W  K  C  D  Y
R  A  I  N  F  O  R  E  S  T  P  G
E  N  O  I  T  I  D  A  R  T  K  R
M  P  E  A  C  Y  G  O  L  O  C  E
O  P  H  N  A  K  P  L  A  N  T  N
N  U  D  U  W  I  H  E  R  B  S  E
Y  N  I  H  C  L  I  S  L  A  N  D
H  A  W  A  I  I  T  H  R  E  A  T
P  Q  L  K  I  L  A  U  E  A  S  U
```

tropical	tradition	herbs	volcano
rain forest	ceremony	threat	pele
Hawaii	island	wildlife	USA
kahuna	ecology	Kilauea	energy
plant	life	puna	

Free Flowing Poem

Select one or two words and try to think of as many related words and ideas as you can. What words did other students choose to write about?

Example:

Kilauea	volcano	active	lava	flow
red	black	smoke	pele	erupt
island	tall	green	sky	sun

GA1460

Jessica Heyn
Girl Scouts Caring for the Earth

On Earth Day 1990, ten artists from the Girl Scout Council of Washington, D.C., had their work exhibited at the National Museum of Women in the Arts. One of those artists was eight-year-old Jessica Heyn from Damascus, Maryland.

The purpose of the contest was to bring about environmental awareness through artistic expression. Hundreds of posters were sent in from girls age five to seventeen. Crayons, markers, paint and collage were just a few of the methods that the contestants used to deliver their environmental messages.

"Girl Scouts Recycle" was the title of the poster that Jessica entered in the contest. She got the idea at church, where she noticed a huge recycling bin. When she got home, she got out her markers and started to draw. After about two hours, she had created a picture of a row of brightly colored houses with a recycling bin out front. Jessica said that she was glad that she could do something to help the environment.

Now two years later, Jessica is still very much interested in art and the environment. She enjoys using watercolors, markers and crayons to create outdoor scenes of people, animals, trees and houses. She also makes sure her family separates the trash and recycles. Her favorite hobbies are horseback riding, science, computers and ballet. Jessica's winning poster delivered a very basic message that helped people to think about their responsibility in caring for the earth.

GA1460

Jessica Heyn Activities
Environmental Art

Jessica Heyn made a statement for the environment in her poster "Girl Scouts Recycle." She used markers to draw her very important message. Create your own environmental art and use many different kinds of materials.

Here are a few of the materials you may want to use:
• Natural things like fallen leaves, pinecones, wood, small pebbles, dirt or sand

• Recycled or reused materials like paper scraps, paper towel tubes, empty containers or cans

• Mediums such as paint, clay, plaster, metal and glue

GA1460

Marianne Riedman

A Love for the Ocean

For as long as she can remember, Marianne Riedman loved the ocean. Marianne grew up in Southern California where she and her father spent many weekends snorkeling and scuba diving in the crystal clear waters near Santa Catalina Island. It was then that she decided to take this fun pastime and make it a full-time career in marine science.

Starting out as a research diver, Marianne traveled to places such as Australia's Great Barrier Reef to study green sea turtles. Back in California she observed the behaviors of the elephant seal on Ano Nuevo Island. Then in 1976, she was asked to help out with one of the first long term studies of California sea otters.

Marianne's job was to capture and tag the otters with a small radio. The radios would allow researchers to study the same group of animals over a long period of time. At first, she thought her task would be easy, but she soon learned that the same strong claws and teeth used for opening crabs, sea urchins and other shellfish were also good for self-defense. Marianne discovered that she could learn much just by watching sea otters raise their young, communicate, and forage for food in their natural habitat.

These days, Marianne is a marine biologist with the Monterey Bay Aquarium in California. Her job is to study sea otters in the wild and in captivity. She says, "I ask questions about the behavior and ecology of the sea otters' natural habitat." The part of her job she enjoys the most is watching the animals at play through binoculars or with a special sighting scope. These instruments allow her to observe the otters closely without disturbing them.

Marianne has done a lot of thinking and studying about the sea otter. She has written ten books and worked with scientists in Russia and Japan to better understand how sea otters in other parts of the world live. In her book, *Sea Otters*, she writes how in the eighteenth and nineteenth centuries, they were hunted down for their furs. Guarded by the Marine Mammal Protection Act and the Endangered Species Act, their population has slowly grown over the years. Marianne Riedman states that the best protection for the animals is prevention. By keeping the ocean free of oil spills and other pollutants, people can not only help protect sea otters, but all life on this planet.

GA1460

Marianne Riedman
Sea Otter Facts

- Sea otters are found mainly in Alaska, Northern California and Russia.

- Sea otters often rest together in groups called "rafts." In Alaska some rafts may contain as many as 2000 animals.

- Young sea otters are called "pups." Pups are mainly born in the water, but sometimes are born on land.

- Sea otters use kelp forests as a source of food and protection. By eating sea urchins and other creatures of the kelp forest, they help to maintain the delicate balance of the nearshore marine community.

- Although they are completely adapted to water, sea otters sometimes "haul out" on land to give birth.

- The blubber and thick fur of sea otters can withstand ocean waters as cold as 35 degrees Fahrenheit.

- Researchers like Marianne Riedman have found that otters, when given a choice, tend to have favorite foods. While one otter may prefer abalone and turban snails, another may choose rock crabs and urchins.

- New findings indicate that sea otters pass on ways of finding food as well as their favorite food choices to their young. One wild otter in Monterey Bay was spotted teaching her young pup to use a bottle to open shellfish.

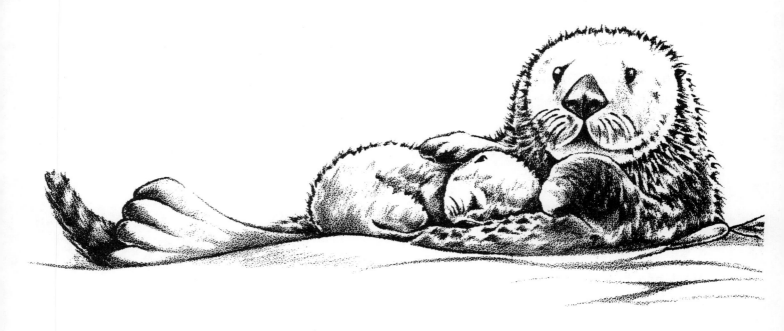

GA1460

Marianne Riedman Activities

- Sea otters are not only cute and furry creatures to watch, but are mammals that are highly adapted to their marine environment.

- Eyes: adapted for both underwater and aerial vision

- Whiskers: used to locate prey

- Paws: used to capture and eat prey and for protection

- Lungs: designed to allow otters to dive to great depths of more than 100 meters, and to maintain surface buoyancy

- Teeth: developed to crush hard shellfish and for protection

- Blubber and fur: used to insulate against cold waters; the warmest fur in the world

- Flippers: used for swimming about easily in the water

```
S  E  A  O  T  T  E  R  S  P  D
E  N  I  R  A  M  K  W  H  A  I
S  P  S  W  A  P  I  S  E  K  V
N  W  S  P  K  M  R  P  L  S  E
I  B  U  P  L  E  K  U  L  A  N
H  C  R  A  B  S  C  P  F  L  A
C  A  L  I  F  O  R  N  I  A  E
R  W  H  I  S  K  E  R  S  P  C
U  L  K  S  T  F  A  R  H  X  O
```

sea otters	rafts	swim
crabs	pups	fur
marine	dive	shellfish
urchins	ocean	kelp
paws	whiskers	Russia
Alaska	California	

Choose three words and create a sentence about sea otters and their marine environment.

GA1460

Naomi Rose

Orca

In the Midwest, thousands of miles away from the nearest ocean, thirteen-year-old Naomi Rose dreamed of working as a marine biologist someday. Naomi knew a lot about marine life. She learned the common names of plants and animals in the ocean, was a member of the Cousteau Society and believed in environmental conservation.

Naomi was determined to make her dream a reality. "I'm a very practical person. I knew that if I wanted to work with marine mammals I would have to take more than biology. I also had to take math, chemistry and physics. I hated those things, but I knew what I wanted and I couldn't ignore those subjects."

Naomi's work in school paid off. Wanting to be sure that marine biology was the right field for her, she contacted Woods Hole Oceanographic Institution in Massachusetts. Naomi went to sea assisting scientists studying marine life in Spain and the Canary Islands for three months. "I took on jobs like standing watch, and earned my food and board on the trip." After that voyage, Naomi was sure that she wanted to be a marine biologist, and started planning her next step.

She decided to continue her studies at the University of Hawaii. There she worked with captive dolphins and found out how the series of clicks, squeaks and whistles made by dolphins are the language they use. One day, Naomi went to one of her teachers and told her about her wish to work in marine science. The teacher told Naomi, "Most students try and get by with doing the minimum. You're different. I believe you!"

Today, Naomi is a marine biologist who studies the behavior of killer whales. Her focus now is on the male of the species. Males travel all of their lives with their mothers. If a male's mother dies before him, he will go to live with his next female relative. This is called "matrifocal," or mother-centered, behavior. Naomi is one of the few people in the world studying the behavior of male killer whales.

She says her parents always suppported her ideas and dreams. "Next to love, trust was the key between me and my parents."

GA1460

Naomi Rose Activities

Killer Whales
Facts from Naomi Rose, Marine Biologist

- Killer whales are top predators. They are at the top of the food chain. That means that nothing naturally kills them except for old age and disease.

- The two most dangerous threats to the survival of killer whales are the same things that threaten all marine mammals. Both threats come from humans:

  As top predators, killer whales get toxins such as DDT, mercury, heavy metal and other poisons into their system. Fish have some toxins in their bodies, and they get eaten by sea lions who also have toxins. Killer whales eat the sea lions and the fish and get a buildup of toxins.

  Killer whales are also threatened by something called habit deprivation. Boat traffic, logging, and other kinds of competition for the waters where the whales live may change their behavior or threaten their lives.

- There are many different kinds of killer whales. Most eat fish, salmon and sea lions.

- We don't really know how many killer whales there are in the world. There may be as many as 100,000.

- A pod is a group of whales. The smallest group of killer whales is called a matrilineal group because it consists of a mother and her offspring.

- Killer whales are a kind of dolphin. Killer whales, like all dolphins, vocalize. Each pod of whales has its own specific set of sound patterns.

- Whales used for profit in aquaria are worth millions of dollars. They are often placed under a great deal of stress to perform according to rigid schedules. Sometimes, they may even develop ulcers and problems not usually found in the wild.

Thinking About the Issues

Some people believe that sea parks that make money from marine mammals can provide a valuable service in educating the public about the value of marine life. Sea parks can help in raising money for environmental causes. These aquaria also have successfully bred killer whales in captivity. Many scientists believe that successful births of a species in captivity are good indicators of an animal's well being.

Some people believe that marine aquaria should only be used for scientific study purposes. They believe that killer whales and other marine mammals are placed under too much stress to perform according to rigid schedules. Some scientists note that many killer whales and dolphins in captivity suffer from ulcers and other problems not found in the wild. They believe that too often the killer whales, worth millions of dollars to sea parks, are just seen as a way to make money.

What do you think?

Sherrie Russell Meline
Wildlife Artist

When Sherrie Michiko Shibata was growing up in Madison, Wisconsin, her art teacher, Virginia Johnson, told her that she had something special. Sherrie's family owned a Japanese import and export business in Madison. Sherrie remembers her parents collecting Japanese art. She believes that having art in her home as a child had a lot to do with the way that she creates art today. "My folks always figured that I'd be in art. I was real fortunate. They backed me up all the way," Sherrie says.

Sherrie and her mom would sometimes bring Japanese dolls or other objects to school. The teachers and students enjoyed learning about Sherrie's heritage, but some made fun of her for being different. Sherrie felt different in a good way; she felt good about being Japanese American, had plenty of friends, and had a special talent in art.

Throughout elementary school, high school and college, Sherrie focused on her art. She tried wood sculpture, collage, painting and many other techniques to explore every kind of art possible. Yet, it was not until much later that she became interested in painting waterfowl.

In the late seventies, Sherrie got married, started raising a family and moved to Mount Shasta, California. Then she began thinking about ways to earn some money. She had always loved the art of painted wood decoys, so she decided to try her hand and paint water birds on laminated wood. One day she set up a booth at a local wildlife art show and sold only one painting. An artist in the next booth suggested she try her painting technique on paper. The change made all the difference in the world, and Sherrie was soon on her way.

When Sherrie paints, her goal is to make the birds as real as possible. To do this she uses photographs and firsthand observation of captive and wild birds to catch the specific markings and personality of each bird. Sherrie has a long list of awards, such as the Ducks Unlimited Gold Palette and Chisel Award, and has won several state wildlife print competitions.

Through her work, she has also become active in many conservation efforts for waterfowl and their habitats. Her contributions, both artistic and as an environmental advocate, have helped to establish protected wetland areas throughout California.

Sherrie Russell Meline has a style all her own. She credits her family, cultural heritage and her teachers for helping to foster "something special" in her.

Sherrie Russell Meline
Wetlands

What do you think when you hear the word "swamp" or "marsh"? Do these words conjure up images of the Swamp Thing dragging itself out of a dark and murky pool? Or do you think of goblins or dogs howling in the moor?

Well, in reality bogs, swamps, sloughs, tidal flats and marshes are just different kinds of wetlands. From Florida's mangrove swamps to Alaska's salt marshes, there are wetlands in nearly every state of the country.

Wetlands play host to a variety of plants and wildlife. The ecosystem of a wetland is especially delicate. A lowering of the water level by even one inch can create changes in the relationship among plants and animals. Yet these natural changes in the ecosystem are a normal part of day-to-day living in the wetlands.

Many wetland areas in the United States are used for recreation. They are places where people can enjoy such pastimes as bird-watching, photography, and often canoeing or kayaking. Some offer hunting and fishing, while others are protected sanctuaries. One popular wetland area is Okefenokee swamp. Crossing the boundaries between southeastern Georgia and Florida, this famous swamp is home to many different kinds of wildlife including bear, deer, raccoons and alligators. Farther west, Elkhorn Slough is a part of the newly established Monterey Bay Sanctuary in California. The waterways along the slough offer people a great place to kayak and observe birds like the snowy white egret.

Wetlands help to remove some of the pollutants from the water we use, and their plants help to produce the oxygen we breathe. Scientific study has also uncovered the medical benefits in some of their plants. Wetlands are cheaper and better than man-made dams at controlling floods, according to the U.S. Army Corps of Engineers.

Some people believe that wetlands are just pools of stagnant water, soggy mud and breeding places for mosquitoes. As a result, many wetland areas are being filled in and developed as sites for businesses and homes. Protection of American wetlands is a big issue for the lawmakers of this country. One of their biggest problems is how to define what exactly is a wetland. In some areas it is clear, like with Okefenokee swamp, but in other areas it's sometimes hard to tell if the area is a real wetland or just a big puddle. Right now, many lawmakers are trying to figure out the definition of a true wetland and working on ways to preserve these important environments.

GA1460

What Is a Wetland?

What is the difference between a wetland and a big puddle?

Wetlands are usually classified into either coastal or freshwater systems. Many different kinds of wetlands are found within these two categories. They include marshes, swamps, bogs, tidal marshes, prairie potholes and wet meadows.

The Council on Environmental Quality has released some interesting facts about the wetlands. Here are just a few of their findings.

Wetlands, like rain forests, are some of the most biologically productive ecosystems.

Nearly one third of the plants and animals listed as being endangered or threatened are sustained by wetlands.

Many animals like saltwater fish and shellfish use wetlands at some point in their life cycle.

Since colonial times, twenty-two of the 50 states have lost at least half of their wetlands. In fact, before people fully understood the value of wetlands, some laws even encouraged their destruction.

Pam Flowers
An Expedition to the North Pole

Pam Flowers likes to go places where she's never been before. In fact, she likes to go where no one has ever been before. In 1991, Pam became the first person known to have taken a dogsled trip alone to the magnetic North Pole.

Many people wondered if Pam, five feet tall and weighing 100 pounds, would be able to make the 350-mile trip. Twice before Pam had tried to get to the geographic pole located 800 miles beyond the magnetic one. The first time her sled flipped over and she broke her shoulder, and the second time an early thaw turned her back. The third time she met up with bears and temperatures of more than 75 degrees below zero, but Pam kept on until she reached her destination. Pam shares the credit with her team of dogs. She says that it was the skill and endurance of her dogs that got her through the trip.

A Japanese man by the name of Naomi Uemura who dogsledded across the Northwest Passage and to the North Pole inspired Pam to try Arctic dogsledding. She also admired Amelia Earhart because she was a woman who was not afraid to try new adventures. Paul Schurke, another Arctic explorer, believes that going solo can put a person in a kind of danger where no one can be saved.

On all of her trips Pam takes extra care that her supplies and equipment are in perfect condition. She layers her clothing and wears an insulated jacket, hat and pants to keep her warm. Some of her tools include a hatchet, a saw, pliers and a pocketknife. The pocketknife comes in handy in many ways, including chipping away at ice, cutting snow blocks for drinking water and cutting food. She makes sure that there is plenty of food for her team of dogs and for herself. Meat, rice, bread, and dried fruit and nuts are basics she takes along. Working out in sub-zero weather, she eats healthy foods to keep up her strength and energy.

For Pam, the glory of her expeditions isn't just being first, it's the adventure itself. She has seen the shimmering coat of a snow-white polar bear and watched the glow of the midnight sun. Pam Flowers is someone who can see the beauty of life in even the harshest and most remote areas on our earth.

81

Pam Flowers Activities
Caring for Animals

Pam Flowers knows that her trip to the magnetic North Pole just wouldn't have been the same without her dogs. She had to depend on her team of dogs to take her there and back. By working with her dogs in a humane way, she built up a working and trusting relationship with them.

The dogs Pam used for her trip can withstand freezing temperatures. The pads on their feet are especially tough, and their fur is very thick. Most of the dogs are at least part Alaskan Husky.

The native people of the North, the Inuit, have used dogs for sledding, carrying cargo and as pets for centuries.

What do you think of the practice of dogsledding? Should it be done at all, or only under certain conditions? What conditions? Write down your opinions and share them with others in class.

Amazing Trek Through the Ice Floe

Beginning at START find your way through the ice floe.

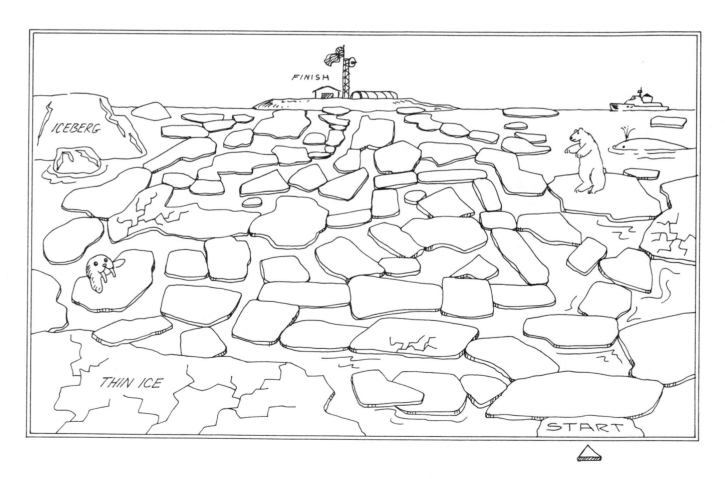

82

Banana Slug News

A newsletter for the slimy at heart   *October 5, 1995•Vol. 1 #1*

Giant Banana Slug Invades Schools in U.S.A.

Sightings of a six-foot banana slug have been reported in several states, including Louisiana, Massachusetts, Nevada and California. Each time the giant yellow creature has been spotted, it has been accompanied by four humans playing string instruments. Sources known only to this reporter claim that the four humans go by the names of "Airy," "Solar," "Dirt" and "Marine," otherwise known as the Banana Slug String Band.

When cornered in Santa Cruz, California, for an interview, "Airy" claimed that the group is only trying to help people understand and care about the earth. He says the group uses music, comedy, theater and puppets to teach science and ecology. That's where the giant banana slug comes in.

The band uses puppets like the banana slug and music to explain just how all living things are related in our world. Songs like "Decomposition" or "Dirt Made My Lunch" get everybody involved in singing and dancing about earth science. Rap, rock and blues are just a few of the styles of music the Banana Slug String Band uses to get their eco-message across. Just imagine your teacher jumping and singing to the happy sounds of "Water Cycle Boogie!"

The Banana Slugs, otherwise known as Larry Graff (Airy), Steve Van Zandt (Solar), Mark Nolan (Marine) and Doug Greenfield (Dirt), all started out as teachers of environmental science. They found they had a talent for singing and playing a multitude of instruments, so they created a new profession for themselves. All of the members take part in writing lyrics and composing music.

"Take the time to wonder," Larry says. "Take care of ourselves, each other and the earth"–a very down-to-earth message from a person who is in tune with the environment.

So it just may happen that the next time you spot a six-foot banana slug giving a concert with its very own band, who knows, it might be at your school! Keep your eyes peeled!

BANANA
·SLUG·
STRING BAND

83   GA1460

Slug Activities

Just like the Banana Slug String Band, you too can tell people about the environment with drama, music and real facts! Choose from one of the skits below, or make up your very own!

Conduct a giant banana slug interview. What is the banana slug concerned about for its habitat and the world?

Create and perform a song about the environment with your friends.

Make a puppet show on recycling. Use recycled and reused products for your puppets.

GA1460

What's in Your Drink Box?

What do you do with your drink box when you're finished drinking the juice? This is the problem that many companies who make drink boxes and environmentalists are trying to work out. On one hand, the drink box companies say that the tough little container is portable, doesn't need to be refrigerated and resists breakage. On the other hand, environmentalists claim that drink boxes are difficult to recycle and add to the country's growing solid waste problem.

Americans throw away drink boxes at a rate of eight million each day. They were first used in this country in the early 1980s. Also known as "aseptic" packaging, the containers are used for juice, milk and sometimes food. Aseptic packaging is portable, sterile and doesn't need refrigeration.

The same construction that makes the drink box work is also the same reason why it is a problem to recycle. Drink boxes are made out of 24 percent plastic, 6 percent aluminum and 70 percent paper. These different layers are fused together. One method of recycling drink boxes currently being tested is called "hydropulping." Hydropulping uses water to separate the layers of the box. The paper recovered is then used to make products like paper towels. The leftover aluminum and plastic mixture is used to produce objects like flowerpots or plastic lumber. The problem with hydropulping is that the boxes don't always separate in the process. Drink box manufacturers say that they are willing to put in the time and the money for testing, but the real problem is in the collection of the containers. Pilot programs for collecting boxes have been started at schools and other institutions in sixteen states.

Maine is one state that has banned aseptic containers. Maine's legislature says that pilot recycling programs are not enough. Maine's law makes it clear that a complete recycling program has to be in place before the ban will be overturned. Many environmentalists agree with Maine's action to ban aseptic containers. Manufacturers claim that the state's lawmakers are unfair to ban what they believe is a useful product. While this recycling debate is being sorted out, students and teachers can work on ideas to reuse the containers in the classroom, start collection programs, or use fewer containers altogether.

GA1460

"What's in Your Drink Box?" Activities

Drink Box Packaging

Design a drink box container that is earth-friendly and can be reused or recycled.

Drink Box Dissection

Cut open a drink box and see if you can identify the different layers.

Soak sections in water to see how easily each layer separates.

POLYETHYLENE

ALUMINUM

PAPER

ZIPPY
DRINK

GA1460

Larry Villella
A Sprinkling of Green

Thirteen-year-old Larry Villella knows that sometimes a little chore can turn into a big job. Larry is the inventor of a new water saving garden device.

The idea came to Larry as he was watering the trees around his house. Watering the trees in the yard was not Larry's idea of fun. He had to move the sprinkler hose every fifteen minutes around the base of the trees to insure even watering. Now, that's not so tough if you have one little tree, but Larry had more than ten that needed water. After a while, Larry said to himself, "This is ridiculous."

Larry got an idea. He decided to modify the design of his existing sprinkler. Using the skills he had learned building models with his dad, he cut out a small section of the sprinkler head and then sealed the ends. The result was a "C" shaped sprinkler that fit perfectly around the trees in his yard.

Larry found that this new sprinkler not only saved time, but also kept the water from going in all different directions. Larry entered his sprinkler in a local invention contest and won the grand prize. Friends and neighbors began showing an interest in his invention and gave him plenty of encouragement. Larry started a new business in the basement of his home, calling it "Conserve Sprinkler." With the help of his mom, dad and three sisters, Larry has sold sprinklers in more than forty states. He has even filled sprinkler orders from countries as far away as England and Portugal.

Experts in the field of agriculture and gardening say that the sprinkler helps to minimize wasteful water runoff and is especially good for use on newly planted trees and shrubs. Larry hopes that his invention will help promote tree planting in the United States and other countries.

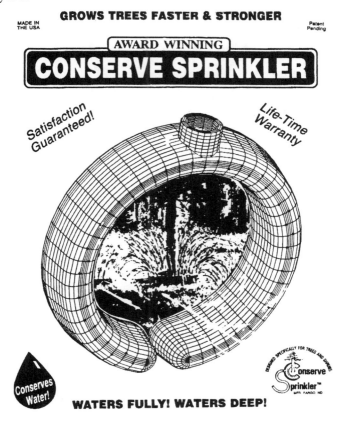

GROWS TREES FASTER & STRONGER

MADE IN THE USA

Patent Pending

AWARD WINNING

CONSERVE SPRINKLER

Satisfaction Guaranteed!

Life-Time Warranty

Conserves Water!

DESIGNED SPECIFICALLY FOR TREES AND SHRUBS

Conserve Sprinkler™ MFR. FARGO, ND

WATERS FULLY! WATERS DEEP!

GA1460

Larry Villella Activities
Conserve Sprinkler

Larry Villella redesigned something that wasn't working well for him and turned it into a useful product for a lot of people. Try some of these activities or create your own!

Help Larry sell the Conserve Sprinkler. Produce a full-page ad for the soil conservation newsletter. Try to catch people's attention with a catchy logo or motto.

Create your own redesigned product. Draw a picture and indicate what makes your new item so special!

Each year, Americans waste a great amount of water. Some areas like California have even been affected by droughts. Think of some ways to conserve water around your house.

Sprinkler Maze

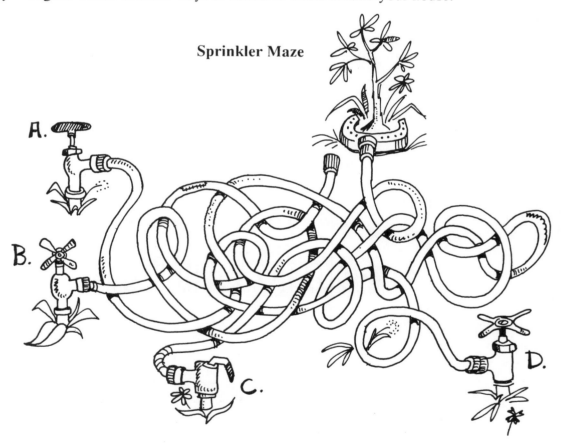

Refer to the Decoding Key on page vi to help you solve the puzzle below.

__ __ __ __ __ __ __ __ __ __ __ __ __ __ __ __ .

Al Lewandowski
When You're Hot, You're Hot!

Renewable Energy Labs in Colorado, and received national recognition for his work on the high-flux solar furnace.

Things really started warming up for Al when he and the other engineers on a project conducted a test one day. In the test they broke a world record. The old record concentrated sunlight more than 17,000 times its normal intensity, but Al and his group recorded an unofficial record of 21,000 times the sun's normal concentration.

The solar furnace works by using mirrors called "flat plate collectors" to direct and concentrate sunlight into usable energy. Sunlight is made up of many different kinds of rays. Some of these rays you can see. They are called visible rays. Other rays like ultraviolet and infrared are invisible. The solar furnace takes the infrared part of sunlight and burns the waste material, while the ultraviolet part deactivates any of the toxins that are left over from the burning process.

Most waste incinerators in use today reach between 600 to 800 degrees centigrade. The problem with these incinerators is that there are gases and chemicals that are not completely broken down and destroyed. These gases and chemicals are then released into the air as toxic pollutants. Al says that the solar furnace is much cheaper to use, cleaner and more efficient.

Al sees the solar furnace as a research tool right now, but he believes that within a few years there will be pilot solar furnace systems working in many parts of the country.

Al's hot idea has turned into something really big. But he still says, *"I just wanted a job where I could focus on something. Something for the environment."*

When Al Lewandowski gets "hot around the collar," watch out! He means business–solar business. Al helped to design a high-flux solar furnace, a new way of disposing of hazardous wastes. Special mirrors are used to concentrate sunlight into energy. Al says that the furnace is so strong it can reach an intensity that is nearly as hot as the surface of the sun.

Al was born in Cleveland, Ohio. He remembers always liking science and math while growing up. In college he became interested in solar energy and worked on projects channeling this very clean and free natural resource. Later, he joined the National

Al Lewandowski Activities
The Spirit of Invention

Inventions create solutions to problems. Benjamin Franklin, George Washington Carver, Jacques Cousteau and Madame Curie are all people who were inventors. Al Lewandowski is another example. He created the high-flux solar furnace to incinerate waste more efficiently than ever before. Use your inventive mind to create something that will help solve an environmental problem in your area.

Think about places in your community where there are environmental problems.

Describe one of these problems and why you think it exists. Draw or write down what the problem looks like, along with a map of the area.

Talk with other students about your problem and find out if they know anything about it. Help them out with the problems they've identified.

Brainstorm some invention ideas on a piece of paper.

Select one of your ideas and draw a blueprint and/or write about it. Be sure to include how your invention or solution might affect the people connected to the problem.

Share your inventions with the class. Talk about your inventions and be open to questions.

Refer to the Decoding Key on page vi to help you solve the puzzle below.

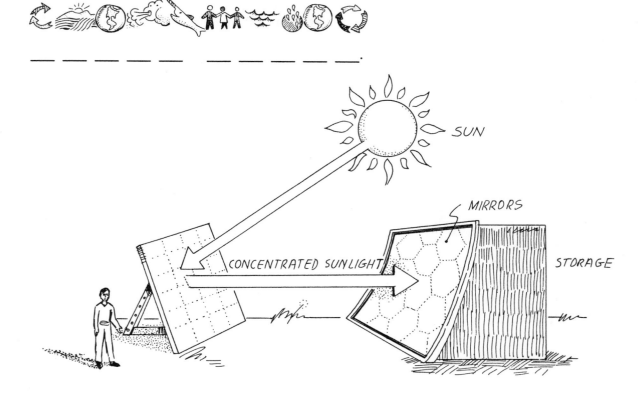

Ward and Maja Smith
A Family of Surfriders

Surfrider Foundation

Ever since Maja Smith was little, she has been active in the Surfrider Foundation. In the early 80s, she would help her dad, Ward, pass out pamphlets about the new organization. As she helped, she discovered a lot of important information about the environment that she still uses today.

When Maja's school announced an upcoming science fair, she and a classmate decided to enter. With the help of her dad, Maja and her friend tested the pollution levels at the mouth of a major river. The tests took several weeks and it often rained. Yet the rain created some interesting test results. The more it rained, the higher the pollution levels in the river. Ward, a science teacher at a local junior high school, guessed that the pollution was coming from sewage overflow. Their hard work paid off, and they won first prize at the science fair. On a trip back to the river, Maja and Ward saw some kids playing in the water. She warned them about the pollution, but they didn't believe her and kept on playing. She remembers, "There weren't even signs posted or anything."

Through the Surfrider Foundation, Ward is developing an easy-to-use water testing program for students. He hopes that they will learn about ways to test the water for pollution and then work on ways to help protect the waters we use for work, play and day-to-day living.

For Maja and Ward, practicing environmentally sound ways of living is second nature. They make use of solar energy to heat the geodesic home that Ward built himself. Recycling, reusing and composting are simply everyday activities. Maja also keeps informed about environmental issues and events through magazines and television programs. Maja and Ward Smith are working in everyday ways to protect our environment.

91

GA1460

Ward and Maja Smith Activities
Surf's Up—Ocean Facts

1. The Pacific Ocean is how many times larger than the size of the United States?

    a. 2 times
    b. 5 times
    c. 10 times
    d. 20 times

2. The Atlantic Ocean is 10 times the size of the United States. Approximately how many square miles is the Atlantic Ocean?

    a. 33,000 square miles
    b. 334,200 square miles
    c. 3,342,000 square miles
    d. 33,342,000 square miles

3. Name the deepest ocean in the world.

    a. Atlantic
    b. Arctic
    c. Indian
    d. Pacific

4. Ferdinand Magellan named the Pacific Ocean. What does the word "Pacific" mean?

    a. pace
    b. peaceful
    c. package
    d. turbulent

5. The ancient Romans believed that the Atlas Mountains were located at the end of the earth. The ocean on the other side of the mountains was called the Atlantic. On what continent are the Atlas Mountains located?

    a. Africa
    b. Australia
    c. Asia
    d. North America

Refer to the Decoding Key on page vi to help you solve the puzzle below.

__ __ __ __ __ __ __ __ __ __ __ __ __

__ __ __ __ __ __.

GA1460

Dayton Hyde
Caring for Wild Creatures

Now Dayton is working on a project called "Operation Stronghold." The goal of this project is to create sanctuaries for wild mustangs. They are areas where wild horses can run free. He was able to get a 12,600-acre sanctuary established in the Black Hills of South Dakota. The sanctuary opened in 1989 with 300 mustangs. His next goal is to get a larger range that can support thousands of horses.

"These wild mustangs are incarcerated in government holding tanks. They are crowded into pens in the middle of nowhere," Dayton says. He believes that the mustangs represent "the spirit of the plains" and that all inhabitants of this earth are equally important. He describes his personal philosophy by saying, "I live with nature."

"Man is only one small part of nature," says Dayton O. Hyde, the author of such books as *Don Coyote, Island of the Loons*, and *One Summer in Montana*. Dayton Hyde writes about nature and creatures of the wild. His books combine a feel for the old West, compassion for wildlife, and gentle humor.

As an Oregon rancher who sometimes lives in South Dakota, Dayton has always been an active conservationist. When he first started ranching, he used pesticides and other chemicals, but after learning and thinking about ecology and how everything in nature is related, he stopped using them. He then built marshes and wetlands on his property. Slowly, birds and other wildlife he had never seen before returned. Coyotes, foxes, ducks and other animals made their home on his property. He started convincing other ranchers and landowners to do the same. After years of hard work he has helped turn more than six million acres of private property into protected wetlands.

Dayton Hyde
Wild Mustangs
The Spirit of the Plains

Mari could easily spot the dappled mare with her flowing mane and tail out of the herd of forty mustangs. Each weekend she and her friend Peter would take their bikes and watch the horses as they grazed or thundered across the floor of the canyon.

Afterwards, they would pretend their bikes were mustangs as they rode back to Mari's house. There they would draw and write stories about the mustangs. Her favorite was the gray mare who would give birth to a foal in the spring. Mari couldn't wait. In just a couple of months, there would be a new addition to the herd.

One evening as Mari sat in the living room drawing the gray mare with her new foal by her side, she turned on the TV news. As she was about to change the channel, she saw the familiar canyon where the mustangs lived. A reporter standing on the canyon rim was talking about how some of the ranchers in the area wanted the horses out. They said that the mustangs were competing with their cattle for water.

Mari was worried. She knew that many wild mustangs were moved to holding pens in Nevada, Texas and Nebraska. Those who could not be adopted would remain in the pens the rest of their lives. A few of the lucky ones would be rescued and sent to protected areas where they could roam freely. She thought about what might happen to the herd and especially the mare who was about to foal. Mari called Peter.

94

GA1460

"They can't do that!" said Peter.

"Yes they can, and they will. The news report said that they'll be rounded up in two weeks and taken to an abandoned missile testing site in Nevada," said Mari.

"What can we do?" said Peter.

"I don't know, but we'll have to act fast!" Mari said.

Mari and Peter promised each other that they would try to think of some ideas that night and bring them up at school the next day. Mari lay her head down on the table where she was drawing. She looked at her stack of drawings and stories about the wild mustangs. She picked up her colored pencils and finished the picture of the pregnant gray mare munching green grass next to a pool of clear water. Drawing seemed to make her feel better. Then she got an idea.

The next day Mari and Peter talked about the plan. They got to school early as their teacher, Mr. Macias, was getting ready for class. Mari and Peter went up to his desk. They opened their backpacks and turned them upside down. Out poured the drawings and stories Mari and Peter had written.

"We want to make a book from our stories," said Mari.

"Yes, and then we want to tell our friends about what's happening with the mustangs in the canyon." continued Peter.

"What a great idea!" said Mr. Macias.

For the next three days, the two kids made a cover, put finishing touches on drawings, and bound the book together. There was a story of how more than three hundred years ago the mustangs had escaped from the Spanish explorers. There were stories of stallions fighting for leadership of the herd, and at the end, Mari's story about the gray mare. The rest of the class wrote letters to the cattle ranchers and the Bureau of Land Management, the group in charge of the move.

When the book was finished, Mr. Macias added his own letter and made three copies of the book and letters. He sent them out to the local cattle ranchers association and the state congress. The last copy he sent to the town newspaper.

By the end of the first week, the whole town was talking about the book and the project to help keep the mustangs in the canyon. Families talked about the issue over dinner, kids talked about it at the playground, and the cattle ranchers talked about it at their Friday meeting. Some agreed that the mustangs should stay, while others thought that they should go. Some didn't like either solution.

When the week of the move came, some ranchers still felt that there wasn't enough water for both the horses and cattle. After a town meeting they agreed to wait until after the foaling season in spring to move the horses out. They also contributed money to take the horses to a sanctuary in South Dakota. The government agency agreed to help and started making plans to move the mustangs.

Mr. Macias talked with the class about the decision. After everyone had a chance to speak, he took his turn. He said that even though the mustangs didn't get to stay in the canyon, the students had made a big difference. He told the group that their concern for the mustangs got people thinking and talking about their future. He said that now the mustangs would at least be able to run free and not be kept in crowded pens for the rest of their days.

The next summer Mari and Peter watched the herd of mustangs for the last time as they grazed near the canyon pond. The gray mare's new foal was a male. He bore the same dappled markings as his mother. He looked up toward the cliff where Mari and Peter were standing and gave a sharp, high-pitched whinny.

Peter looked at Mari and said, "I think he just thanked us."

96

Toxic Town and Tidy Town
Teacher Guide

The Toxic Town and Tidy Town activity section was designed to promote thinking and talking about the different ways people view the environment. On one level, the towns are polarized: Toxic Town demonstrates a clear disregard for the environment, and Tidy Town reflects more environmentally conscious practices. Yet on another level, the two towns are undeniably linked through the natural resources they share. The complexity of environmental issues can be explored through these activities.

Map

The map of Toxic Town and Tidy Town can be colored and labeled. Children may want to use descriptive terms such as the "Don't Give a Hoot Timber Mill" or "EcoElementary School" to identify buildings and other places in the towns.

Children may also want to create their own versions or get together with other students and create a mural.

Toxic Town and Tidy Town: A Tale of Two Communities

In this activity, students are encouraged to examine the possible ways that environmental problems may occur within communities. Children are asked to think about social values in relationship to the environment and create solutions.

Sharing the stories of how Any Town became divided is just as important as discussing possible solutions. Most likely, a variety of solutions will be volunteered, including keeping both towns separate. The intent of this activity is not to create a happy ending necessarily, but to allow the genuine voices of children to be heard.

Toxic Town and Tidy Town Adventures

These activities can be used as points for a brief discussion or extended over a period of several days. Identifying problems and discussing solutions are the focus of these "adventures."

Teachers may want to first ask for and act upon children's ideas about their own "T" Town adventures before presenting the activities on the following pages.

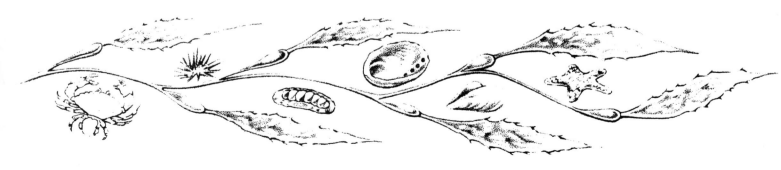

GA1460

Toxic Town

Tidy Town

GA1460

Toxic Town and Tidy Town Adventures

Adventure 1

There is trouble at the mouth of the Weallsharethesame River. Pollutants from many different sources are making people and animals sick. You and your friends have been chosen to pinpoint the three major causes of pollution in the river.

Your job is to describe in detail how you discovered the source of the pollution.

Adventure 2

You are a finalist in the Tidy Town EcoAward Contest. The judges ask you to describe your invention and explain why it will help the earth. Draw a sketch of your invention and write or give your speech.

Adventure 3

Using maps of your local area and the Toxic Town and Tidy Town maps, draw your own community. Indicate areas where there is heavy traffic or the possibility for environmental problems.

GA1460

More Toxic Town and Tidy Town Adventures

Try out some of these discussion and writing activities or create your own "T" Town Adventures!

Adventure 1

You and your group have been appointed to assess the environmental situation in both Toxic Town and Tidy Town. Identify the environmental problems and solutions in each community. Use the town map as a guide.

Adventure 2

The kids in Toxic Town and Tidy Town have gotten together and decided to work on a project that will help both communities. They have a list of at least ten different projects that they feel will help clean up the environment and bring the people of both towns together.

Create that list and then describe the project the group decided to work on.

Adventure 3

The people of Toxic Town and Tidy Town have decided to hold a meeting to discuss the possibility of building a bridge across the Weallsharethesame River. Some people think that the bridge will help the two communities to get along better and make traveling to other areas more convenient. Others believe that a bridge will only create more problems for both towns.

You have been asked to be the recorder for the meeting. Your job is to write what each person said in the meeting and describe the final decision.

```
Tips
√ Use people from your class to role-play the part of town members.
√ Let all people make up names and identify themselves before stating their opinions.
```

GA1460

EcoActivities

_____

_____

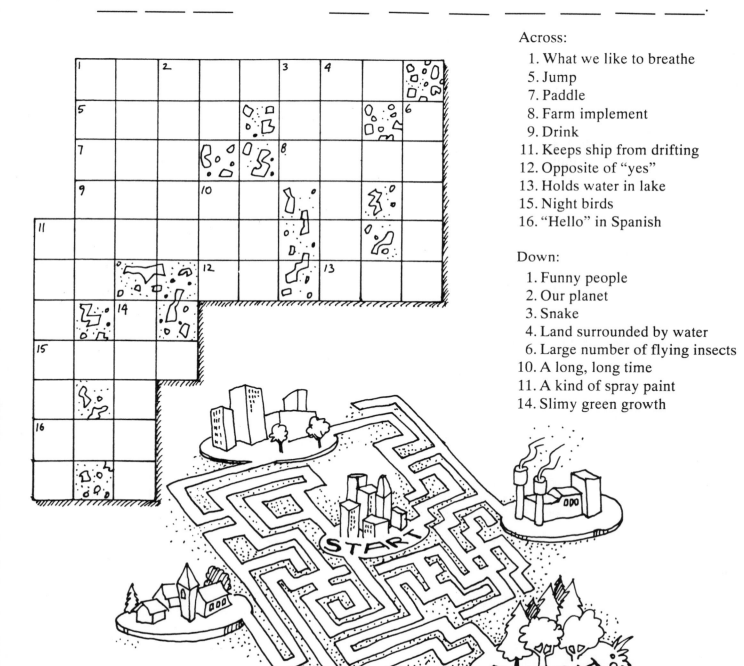

Across:
1. What we like to breathe
5. Jump
7. Paddle
8. Farm implement
9. Drink
11. Keeps ship from drifting
12. Opposite of "yes"
13. Holds water in lake
15. Night birds
16. "Hello" in Spanish

Down:
1. Funny people
2. Our planet
3. Snake
4. Land surrounded by water
6. Large number of flying insects
10. A long, long time
11. A kind of spray paint
14. Slimy green growth

GA1460

Teacher Resources
Selected Resources: Environmental Organizations

American Forestry Association
P.O. Box 2000
Washington, DC 20013
Tel 202-667-3300
Purpose: To maintain and improve the health of trees and forests through education on a global level

American Horse Protection Association, Inc.
P.O. Box 1266
Denver, CO 80201
Tel 303-7942-9900
Purpose: To protect the welfare of wild and domestic horses through public education

Aseptic Packaging Council
1000 Potomac St. NW
Suite 401
Washington, DC 20007
Tel 202-333-5900
Purpose: To educate the public about the many uses of aseptic packaging

Citizen's Clearinghouse for Hazardous Waste
P.O. Box 926
Arlington, VA 22216
Tel 703-276-7070
Purpose: Founded by Louise Gibbs, the community activist who helped to alert the citizens of Love Canal, New York, about the hazardous waste dump located beneath their homes. The Citizen's Clearinghouse informs the public about toxic chemicals and their impact on people and the environment.

The Cousteau Society
8440 Santa Monica Blvd.
Los Angeles, CA 90069-4221
Tel 213-656-4422
Purpose: Organization committed to the protection and preservation of the earth and its people

GA1460

Earth Island Institute
300 Broadway, Suite 28
San Francisco, CA 94133
Tel 415-788-3666
Purpose: Develops innovative environmental projects for the conservation, preservation and restoration of the earth

Goldman Environmental Foundation
1160 Battery Street, Suite 400
San Francisco, CA 94111
Tel 415-788-1090
Purpose: International award foundation for notable work for the environment

Rachel Carson Council
8940 Jones Mill Road
Chevy Chase, MD 20815
Tel 301-652-1877
Purpose: Committed to informing the public about the use and abuse of chemical pesticides and other toxic chemicals

Sheri Griffith Expeditions
P.O. Box 1324
Moab, UT 84532
Tel 801-259-8229
Purpose: Ecologically–minded river rafting trips and international adventures

Surfrider Foundation
P.O. Box 2704 #86
Huntington Beach, CA 92467
Tel 714-960-8390
Purpose: To protect, enhance and enjoy the world's ocean coastal resources

TreePeople
12601 Mulholland Drive
Beverly Hills, CA 90210
Tel 818-753-4600
Purpose: To plant and maintain trees and encourage sound environmental practices for children and adults

Every effort has been made, at the time of publication, to insure the accuracy of the information included in this book. We cannot guarantee, however, that the agencies and organizations we have mentioned will continue to operate or to maintain these current locations indefinitely.

GA1460

Answer Key

Black Elk Activities Page 3

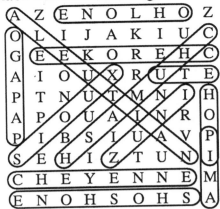

Rachel Carson Activities Page 33

BE CAREFUL WITH PESTICIDES.

Jacques Cousteau Activities Page 37

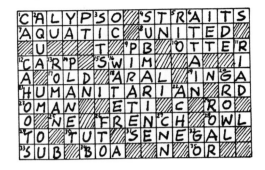

Graceanna Lewis Activities Page 6

BIO MEANS LIFE.

Henry David Thoreau Activities Page 8

BE EARTHWISE WHEN YOU BUY.

Mary Hunter Austin Activities Page 13

ecology   world   earth   nature   bush
trees   insects   water   solar
soil   compost   birds   wild

Mardy and Olaus Murie Activities Page 18

1. porcupine, 2. skunk, 3. snake, 4. squirrel,
5. moose, 6. fish

Aldo Leopold Activities Page 21

1. true, 2. true, 3. false, 4. true, 5. true

David Brower Activities Page 41

FRIENDS OF EARTH

Andy Lipkis Activities Page 43

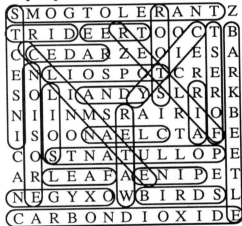

Conduct a Survey! Page 49

kayaking, sailing, scuba diving, rock climbing, river rafting, skiing, ballooning, surfing, hang gliding, mountain biking, running, hiking, horseback riding

Roger Tory Peterson Activities Page 24

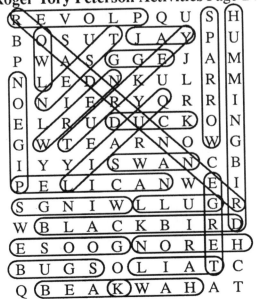

Juliana Furtado Activities Page 53

GA1460

Sheri Griffith Activities Page 55

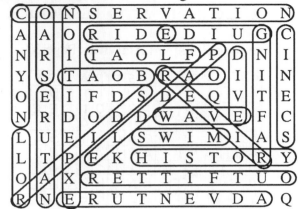

Marianne Riedman Activities Page 75

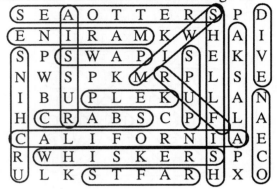

Larry Villella Activities Page 88
CONSERVE   WATER.

Al Lewandowski Activities Page 90
CLEAN   POWER

Ward and Maja Smith Activities Page 92
1. d
2. d
3. d
4. b
5. a
KEEP OUR OCEANS CLEAN.

EcoActivities Page 102
SOLVE   THESE   FUN   PUZZLES.

Sheri Griffith Activities Page 56

Miliani Trask Activities Page 70

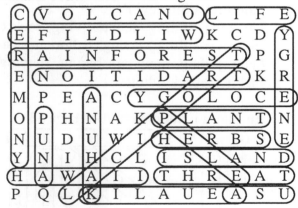

GA1460